Probability Problems a.
by Stefan Hollos and J. Rich
ISBN 978-1-887187-14-5

Copyright ©2013 by Exstrom Laboratories LLC

Abrazol Publishing

an imprint of Exstrom Laboratories LLC
662 Nelson Park Drive, Longmont, CO 80503-7674 U.S.A.

About the Cover

Cover created with the help of POV-Ray and Inkscape. We thank the creators and maintainers of this excellent software.

Contents

There is a very fundamental aspect to probability theory. The most accurate and complete description that we have of the physical world is called quantum mechanics. The most famous equation in quantum mechanics is called the Schrodinger equation which allows you to solve for something called a wave function. If you take the square magnitude of a wave function you get a probability distribution. These probability distributions are in a sense very real. They can for example predict how atoms bond to each other to form chemical compounds. At its most fundamental level, chemistry is based on probability distributions.

Probability has many uses beyond physics and chemistry. It is used in computer science, engineering, biology, finance, games of chance, and in everyday life. It is considered by some to be a form of generalized logic (see for example E. T. Jaynes, Probability Theory: The Logic of Science). Probability theory is one of the most applied areas of mathematics and learning how to solve probability problems is a skill that can be used in many areas.

We enjoy solving probability problems. Why? Because there is an almost endless variety of interesting and stimulating problems to choose from. If you like puzzles then you will enjoy solving these problems. Not only is it just plain intellectual fun but it will sharpen your reasoning and problem solving skills.

This book deals primarily with discrete probability problems. These are problems that can be solved with very little mathematical background. A good grasp of algebra is required and some previous exposure to probability or combinatorics is helpful. We have included sections that review the basics of discrete probability and combinatorics. If you are already familiar with these then you can go directly to the problems.

Also included are sections on more advanced topics in discrete probability that are helpful in solving some of the more difficult and interesting problems. There is a section on how to calculate probabilities when you have a set of events that are nonexclusive, meaning that more than one of the events can occur simultaneously. There is a section on solving Bayesian type problems. These are problems where the probability of a hypothesis is calculated based on some evidence. A simple example is the hypothesis that a die is loaded with the evidence being the result of rolling the die repeatedly. There is a section on solving collection problems. A simple example of this kind of problem is calculating the probability that it takes more than 10 rolls of a die to get all six faces at least once. Another example is calculating the average number of boxes of cereal you need to buy to collect all the different prizes inside. The final introductory section is on solving run problems. The canonical example here is calculating the average number of times you need to toss a coin to get n heads in a row.

After the introductory sections come the problems. They generally increase in difficulty as you go and are grouped together somewhat by type. The first few are very easy and you should consider them warmups for what's to come. Some of the later problems are very challenging and will require significant work to solve. Many of the problems are modernized versions of the problems and exercises found in the book: ***Choice and Chance*** by W. A. Whitworth (see Further Reading at the end of the book). Happy problem solving.

We can be reached by email at:
stefan[at]exstrom DOT com
richard[at]exstrom DOT com
Stefan Hollos and J. Richard Hollos
Exstrom.com
QuantWolf.com
Exstrom Laboratories LLC
Longmont, Colorado, U.S.A.
April 2013

Discrete probability is concerned with observations, experiments or actions that have a finite or countably infinite number of unpredictable outcomes. Countably infinite means the outcomes can be counted or labeled by the natural numbers, $1, 2, 3, \ldots$. The set of all possible outcomes is called the sample space (standard terminology) and is denoted by the symbol Ω. An element of Ω (an individual outcome) will be denoted by ω. A coin toss for example, has two possible outcomes: heads (H) or tails (T). The sample space is $\Omega = \{H, T\}$ and $\omega = H$ is one of the possible outcomes. Another example is the roll of a die which has 6 outcomes so that $\Omega = \{1, 2, 3, 4, 5, 6\}$. A subset of the sample space is called an event and is denoted by a capital letter such as A or B. In the die example, let A be the event that an even number is rolled, then $A = \{2, 4, 6\}$.

Each outcome, ω, has a probability assigned to it, denoted $P(\omega)$. The probability is a real number ranging from 0 to 1 that signifies the likelihood that an outcome will occur. If $P(\omega) = 0$ then ω will never occur and if $P(\omega) = 1$ then ω will always occur. An intermediate value such as $P(\omega) = 1/2$ means that ω will occur roughly half the time if the experiment is repeated many times. In general, if you perform the experiment a large number of times, N, and the number of times that ω occurs is $n(\omega)$, then the ratio $n(\omega)/N$ should ap-

proximately equal the probability of ω. It is possible
to define $P(\omega)$ as the limit of this ratio.

$$P(\omega) = \lim_{N \to \infty} \frac{n(\omega)}{N} \tag{1}$$

In other words, if you could repeat the experiment an
infinite number of times, the fraction of the time that
the outcome is ω, is the probability of ω.

The function $P(\omega)$, which assigns probabilities to outcomes, is called a probability distribution. We will now
look at some of its properties. To begin with, if the
probabilities are defined as in equation 1, then clearly
the sum of all probabilities must equal 1.

$$\sum_{\omega \in \Omega} P(\omega) = 1 \tag{2}$$

It is often necessary to determine the probability that
one of a subset of all the possible outcomes will occur.
If A is a subset of Ω then $P(A)$ is the probability that
one of the outcomes contained in A will occur. Using
the definition in 1 it should be obvious that:

$$P(A) = \sum_{\omega \in A} P(\omega) \tag{3}$$

Many other properties can be derived from the algebra

of sets. Let $A + B$ be the set of all elements in either A or B (no duplicates) and let AB be the the set of all elements in both A and B, then:

$$P(A + B) = P(A) + P(B) - P(AB) \qquad (4)$$

If A and B have no elements in common then they are exclusive events, i.e. they can not both occur simultaneously. In this case equation 4 reduces to $P(A+B) = P(A) + P(B)$. In general, the probability that any one of a number of exclusive events will occur is just equal to the sum of their individual probabilities.

Conditional probabilities and the closely related concept of independence are very important and useful in probability calculations. Let $P(A|B)$ be the probability that A has occurred given that we know B has occurred. In short, we will refer to this as the probability of A given B or the probability of A conditioned on B. What $P(A|B)$ really represents is the probability of A using B as the sample space instead of Ω. If A and B have no elements in common then $P(A|B) = 0$. If they have all elements in common so that $A = B$ then obviously $P(A|B) = 1$. If A is a subset of B, meaning that every element of A is also an element of B, then $P(A|B) = P(A)/P(B)$. In the general case we have:

$$P(A|B) = \frac{P(AB)}{P(B)} \qquad (5)$$

Using a single fair die roll as an example, let $A = \{1,3\}$ and $B = \{3,5\}$ then $AB = \{3\}$, $P(AB) = 1/6$, $P(B) = 1/3$ and

$$P(A|B) = \frac{1/6}{1/3} = \frac{1}{2} \qquad (6)$$

Knowledge that B has occurred has increased the probability of A from $P(A) = 1/3$ to $P(A|B) = 1/2$. The result can also be deduced by simple logic. We know that B has occurred, therefore the roll was either a 3 or a 5. Half of the B events are caused by a 3 and half by a 5 but only the 3 counts as an A event, therefore $P(A|B) = 1/2$.

Conditional probabilities are not necessarily symmetric. $P(B|A)$ need not be equal to $P(A|B)$. Using the definition in equation 5, you can show that

$$P(A|B)P(B) = P(B|A)P(A) \qquad (7)$$

so the two conditional probabilities are only equal if $P(A) = P(B)$. Another useful thing to keep in mind is that conditional probabilities obey the same properties as non-conditional probabilities. This means for example that if A and B are exclusive events then $P(A + B|C) = P(A|C) + P(B|C)$.

The concept of independence is naturally related to

conditional probability. Two events are independent if the occurrence of one has no effect on the probability of the other. In terms of conditional probabilities this means that $P(A|B) = P(A)$. Independence is always symmetric, if A is independent of B then B is independent of A. Using the definition in equation 5 you can see that independence also implies that

$$P(AB) = P(A)P(B) \tag{8}$$

This is often taken as the defining relation for independence.

Another important concept in probability is the law of total probability. Let the sample space Ω be partitioned by the sets B_1 and B_2 so that every element in Ω is in one and only one of the two sets and we can write $\Omega = B_1 + B_2$. This means that the occurrence of A coincides with the occurrence of B_1 or B_2 but not both and we can write

$$A = AB_1 + AB_2 = A(B_1 + B_2) = A\Omega \tag{9}$$

The probability of A is then

$$P(A) = P(AB_1) + P(AB_2) \tag{10}$$

This can be extended to any number of sets that partition Ω.

Doing any kind of probabilistic analysis usually requires random variables. A random variable is a bit like the probability distributions discussed above in that it assigns a number to each of the elements in the sample space. It is therefore really more like a function that maps elements in the sample space to real numbers. A random variable is usually denoted with an upper case letter such as X and the values it can assume are given subscripted lower case letters such as x_i for $i = 1, 2, \ldots, n$ where n is the number of possible values. The mapping from an element ω to a value x_i is denoted as $X(\omega) = x_i$. Note that it is not necessary that every element be assigned a unique value and the particular value assigned will depend on what you want to analyze.

A simple example is a coin toss betting game. You guess what the result of the toss will be. If your guess is correct you win \$1 otherwise you loose \$1. The sample space consists of only two elements, a correct guess and an incorrect guess $\Omega = \{\text{correct}, \text{incorrect}\}$. If you are interested in analyzing the amounts won and lost by playing several such games then the obvious choice for the random variable is $X(\text{correct}) = 1$, $X(\text{incorrect}) = -1$. If you are just interested in the number of games won or lost then the random variable $Y(\text{correct}) = 1$, $Y(\text{incorrect}) = 0$ would be better. Often an analysis in terms of one variable can be converted into another variable by finding a relation between them. In the above example $X = 2Y - 1$ could be used to convert between the variables.

As another example consider tossing a coin three times. The sample space consists of 8 elements
$$\Omega = \{TTT, TTH, THT, THH, HTT, HTH, HHT, HHH\}$$
where T indicates the toss was a tail and H a head. This time we let X be the random variable that counts the number of heads in the three tosses. It can have values 0, 1, 2, or 3 and not every element in the sample space has a unique value. The values are $X(TTT) = 0$, $X(TTH) = X(THT) = X(HTT) = 1$, $X(THH) = X(HTH) = X(HHT) = 2$, $X(HHH) = 3$.

Probability distributions are most often expressed in terms of the values that a random variable can take. The usual notation is

$$P(X = x_i) = p(x_i) \tag{11}$$

The function $p(x_i)$ is the probability distribution for the random variable X. It is often also called the probability mass function. Note that it is not necessarily the same as the probability distribution for the individual elements of the sample space since multiple elements may be mapped to the same value by the random variable. In the three coin toss example, each element in the sample space has a probability of 1/8, assuming a fair coin. The probability distribution for X however is $p(0) = 1/8$, $p(1) = 3/8$, $p(2) = 3/8$, $p(3) = 1/8$. It will always be true that the sum over all the probabilities must equal 1.

$$\sum_i p(x_i) = 1 \qquad (12)$$

The two most important properties of a random variable are its expectation (also called mean) and variance. The expectation is simply the average value of the random variable. In the coin toss betting game, X can have a value of +1 or -1 corresponding to winning or losing. In N flips of the coin let k be the number of wins and $N - k$ the number of losses. The total amount won is then

$$W = k - (N - k) \qquad (13)$$

and the average amount won per flip is

$$\frac{W}{N} = \frac{k}{N} - (1 - \frac{k}{N}) \qquad (14)$$

As the number of flips becomes very large the ratio k/N will equal $p(1)$, the probability of winning, and the equation then becomes equal to the expectation of the random variable.

$$E[X] = p(1) - p(-1) \qquad (15)$$

Where $p(-1) = 1 - p(1)$ is the probability of losing and $E[X]$ is the usual notation for the expectation of X. In this case the expectation is the average amount that you can expect to win per flip if you play the game for a very long time.

In general if X can take on n values, x_i, $i = 1, 2, \ldots, n$ with corresponding probabilities $p(x_i)$ then the expectation is

$$E[X] = \sum_{i=1}^{n} p(x_i)x_i \qquad (16)$$

The expectation gives you the average, but in reality large deviations from the average may be possible. The variance of a random variable gives a sense for how large those deviations can be. It measures the average of the squares of the deviations. The equation for the variance is:

$$\mathrm{Var}[X] = \sum_{i=1}^{n} p(x_i)(x_i - E[X])^2 \qquad (17)$$

The equation simplifies somewhat to

$$\text{Var}[X] = E[X^2] - E[X]^2 \qquad (18)$$

where

$$E[X^2] = \sum_{i=1}^{n} p(x_i)x_i^2 \qquad (19)$$

is the expectation for the square of the random variable. In general the expectation for any function, $g(X)$, of the random variable is:

$$E[g(X)] = \sum_{i=1}^{n} p(x_i)g(x_i) \qquad (20)$$

Another useful measure of deviation from the average is called the standard deviation, σ. It is found by taking the square root of the variance.

$$\sigma = \sqrt{\text{Var}[X]} \qquad (21)$$

As we saw above, a sample space can have more than one random variable defined on it. If we have two variables X and Y then we can define the probability that

$X = x_i$ at the same time that $Y = y_j$. This is called the joint probability distribution for X and Y.

$$P(X = x_i, Y = y_j) = p(x_i, y_j) \qquad (22)$$

The individual distributions, $p(x_i)$ and $p(y_j)$, are recovered by summing the joint distribution over one of the variables. To get $p(x_i)$ you sum $p(x_i, y_j)$ over all the possible values of Y.

$$p(x_i) = \sum_j p(x_i, y_j) \qquad (23)$$

and likewise for $p(y_j)$

$$p(y_j) = \sum_i p(x_i, y_j) \qquad (24)$$

From these last two equations it is obvious that if you sum over both variables of the distribution, the result should equal 1.

$$\sum_i \sum_j p(x_i, y_j) = 1 \qquad (25)$$

It is possible to construct a joint distribution for any number of random variables, not just 2. For example

$p(x_i, y_j, z_k)$ would be a joint distribution for the variables X, Y, and Z.

With a joint distribution you can calculate the expectation and variance for functions of variables. The expectation for the sum $X + Y$ is:

$$
\begin{aligned}
E[X + Y] &= \sum_i \sum_j p(x_i, y_j)(x_i + y_j) \qquad (26) \\
&= \sum_i x_i \sum_j p(x_i, y_j) + \sum_j y_j \sum_i p(x_i, y_j) \\
&= \sum_i x_i p(x_i) + \sum_j y_j p(y_j) \\
&= E[X] + E[Y]
\end{aligned}
$$

The property that the expectation for a sum of variables is equal to the sum of their expectations is called linearity and it is true for the sum of any number of variables. For three variables for example $E[X + Y + Z] = E[X] + E[Y] + E[Z]$. Another easily verifiable consequence of linearity is that for any constants a and b

$$
E[aX + bY] = aE[X] + bE[Y] \qquad (27)
$$

In the example of the coin toss game we had two random variables that were related by $X = 2Y - 1$. The linearity property of the expectation means that $E[X] = 2E[Y] - 1$, where we used the fact that the expectation of a constant is just the constant.

The expectation for the product XY is

$$E[XY] = \sum_i \sum_j p(x_i, y_j) x_i y_j \qquad (28)$$

If the variables X and Y are independent then the joint distribution can be factored into a product of the individual distributions, $p(x_i, y_j) = p(x_i)p(y_j)$. In this case you can show that the expectation of the product is the product of the expectations, $E[XY] = E[X]E[Y]$.

For the variance of a sum we have

$$\text{Var}[X + Y] = E[(X - E[X] + Y - E[Y])^2] \qquad (29)$$

after expanding and simplifying this becomes

$$\text{Var}[X + Y] = \text{Var}[X] + \text{Var}[Y] + 2\text{Cov}[X, Y] \qquad (30)$$

where $\text{Cov}[X, Y]$ is called the covariance of X and Y. The covariance is defined as:

$$\text{Cov}[X, Y] = E[XY] - E[X]E[Y] \qquad (31)$$

For independent variables the covariance is zero. The variance of the sum is then just the sum of the variances.

This completes the review of discrete probability. Some additional, more advanced topics, are included in the following sections. To go into the subject in more depth, see the references.

Combinatorics is the art of counting things. There are many problems in discrete probability that boil down to finding the number of ways something can occur and for this you need basic combinatorics. The following is a short review of elementary combinatorics. For more details see our book: *Combinatorics Problems and Solutions*.

One of the most basic principles in counting is the product rule. It says that if you have k sets with sizes n_1 through n_k then the number of ways to select one element from each set is:

$$N = n_1 \cdot n_2 \cdot n_3 \cdots n_k \qquad (32)$$

If all elements are of size n then this simplifies to $N = n^k$. Counting the number of ways a roll of k dice can occur is a simple example of using this principle. You can think of each of the k die as being a set of size 6 and a roll of the die corresponds to randomly selecting one of the elements. The number of ways to select one element from k sets of size 6 is 6^k.

The number of permutations of n objects is the number of ways they can be arranged in linear order. There are n choices for the first in line, $n - 1$ choices for the second, and so on. The number of permutations is then $n! = n \cdot (n - 1) \cdot (n - 2) \cdots 2 \cdot 1$. The number of permutations of n objects taken k at a time is $\frac{n!}{(n-k)!}$. This is the number of ways that k objects can be selected from n objects where the order of selection matters. It is the number of lists of length k that can be made from a set of n objects.

In a circular permutation the elements are arranged in a circular order. There is no natural beginning or end of the arrangement and any circular shift of the elements around the circle does not count as a new arrangement. There are $(n-1)!$ circular permutations of n elements as opposed to $n!$ linear permutations. To see this, pick a point on the circle to correspond with the start of a linear permutation. If you put one of the linear permutations on the circle then every one of its n possible circular shifts will correspond to a different linear permutation when read from the starting point but each of these shifts is counted as the same circular permutation. For every circular permutation there are n linear permutations, therefore the number of circular permutations must be $\frac{n!}{n} = (n-1)!$.

The same argument applies to the number of circular permutations of n elements taken k at a time. There are k circular shifts of the k elements that correspond to different linear permutations but the same circular permutation. So to get the number of circular permutations, divide the linear permutations by k to get $\frac{n!}{k(n-k)!}$.

A combination of n elements taken k at a time is a

k element subset of the n elements. It differs from a permutation of n elements taken k at a time in that the order of the k elements is irrelevant. The number of such combinations is

$$\frac{n!}{k!(n-k)!} = \binom{n}{k} \tag{33}$$

Equivalently, we can say that this gives the number of ways that a set of n elements can be divided into 2 subsets containing k and $n-k$ elements (remember that the elements in a set or subset have no intrinsic order). The term on the right side of equation 33 is called a binomial coefficient. It counts the number of ways you can put k identical balls into n bins with no more than one ball in each bin.

Suppose we want to divide the n element set into 3 subsets with k, l and $n-k-l$ elements. First divide the set into a k element subset and a $n-k$ element subset. This can be done in $\binom{n}{k}$ ways. Next select the l elements for the second subset from the $n-k$ element subset. This can be done in $\binom{n-k}{l}$ ways. Now we have 3 subsets of the original n elements of size k, l, and $n-k-l$. The number of ways of doing this is:

$$\begin{aligned}
\binom{n}{k}\binom{n-k}{l} &= \frac{n!}{k!(n-k)!}\frac{(n-k)!}{l!(n-k-l)!} \\
&= \frac{n!}{k!l!(n-k-l)!} \tag{34}
\end{aligned}$$

You can extend this to any number of subsets. Let's

say we want r subsets with k_i elements in the ith subset. All n elements appear in one of the subsets, therefore $k_1 + k_2 + \cdots + k_r = n$. The number of ways the subsets can be formed is

$$\binom{n}{k_1}\binom{n - k_1}{k_2} \cdots \binom{n - k_1 - k_2 - \cdots - k_{r-1}}{k_r} \quad (35)$$

When this equation is written out and simplified, it becomes

$$\frac{n!}{k_1! k_2! \cdots k_r!} = \binom{n}{k_1, k_2, \cdots, k_r} \quad (36)$$

The term on the right side of this equation is called a multinomial coefficient. It counts the number of ways you can put n balls into r bins so that bin i contains k_i balls. It also counts the number of words of length n you can construct from an alphabet of r kinds of letters with k_i copies of letter i.

One more counting problem that sometimes appears in discrete probability problems is finding the number of ways to put n identical balls into m bins. The number of ways to do it with no restrictions is

$$\binom{n + m - 1}{m - 1} \quad (37)$$

The number of ways to do it so that each bin has at least one ball is

$$\binom{n - 1}{m - 1} \quad (38)$$

For details on these equations and more, see our book *Combinatorics Problems and Solutions*.

A set of events is mutually exclusive when no two of them can occur at the same time. In this case the probability that any one of them occurs is just the sum of their individual probabilities. When they are not mutually exclusive the probability calculation is not as easy. Take for example a dice roll where there are 6 elements in the sample space $(1, 2, 3, 4, 5, 6)$. We can define two events $A_1 = (2, 4, 6)$ and $A_2 = (5, 6)$. The element 6 appears in both events so the probability of A_1 or A_2 occurring is not simply the sum of their individual probabilities because this would count the probability of 6 twice. We will show how to calculate the probability in cases like this where the events are not necessarily mutually exclusive. We start with simple examples of two and three events and then generalize to any number of events.

Figure 1 shows another example of two events where $A_1 = (1, 2, 4, 5, 8, 9, 10)$ has 7 elements, $A_2 = (3, 4, 6, 7, 8)$ has 5 elements and they have elements $(4, 8)$ in common. We want to know the probability of A_1 or A_2 occurring. With no elements in common we could just sum their individual probabilities but doing so would count the probability of $(4, 8)$ twice. This means we have to subtract the probability of the elements common to both events. It is clear then that the general

25

formula for the probability of two events must be:

$$P(A_1 \cup A_2) = P(A_1) + P(A_2) - P(A_1 \cap A_2) \quad (39)$$

where $P(A_1 \cap A_2)$ is the probability of the elements the two events have in common or in other words the probability that both A_1 and A_2 occur simultaneously.

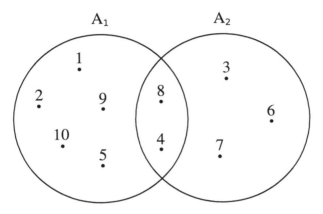

Figure 1: Two set example.

Figure 2 shows an example of three events. It is similar to the two event example but now there is a third event $A_3 = (4, 5, 7, 11, 12)$ with 5 elements. A_3 has two elements in common with both A_1 and A_2 and there is one element that is common to all three events. Summing the probabilities of the three events would count the probability of elements $(5, 7, 8)$ twice and the probability of element 4 three times. Subtracting probabilities common to pairs of events will zero out the probability of element 4 completely since it is common to all three events. This means the probability for 4 has to be added back after the subtractions. It is clear then that the general formula for the probability of three events must be:

$$P(A_1 \cup A_2 \cup A_3) = \qquad (40)$$
$$P(A_1) + P(A_2) + P(A_3)$$
$$-P(A_1 \cap A_2) - P(A_1 \cap A_3) - P(A_2 \cap A_3)$$
$$+P(A_1 \cap A_2 \cap A_3)$$

where $P(A_1 \cap A_2 \cap A_3)$ is the probability of the elements that are common to all three events.

Generalizing further, we can calculate the probability of any of n events occurring with the following formula:

$$P(A_1 \cup A_2 \cup \cdots A_n) = \qquad (41)$$
$$\sum_{k=1}^{n} (-1)^{k-1} \sum_{j_1, j_2, \cdots, j_k} P(A_{j_1} \cap A_{j_2} \cap \cdots A_{j_k})$$

where the inner summation is over all k element subsets of the index set $(1, 2, \ldots, n)$. To prove this formula you only have to show that any element in the union adds its probability only once to sum. We will give a simple sketch of the proof. It is not necessary to follow the proof in order to use the formula. Equation 41 should be almost intuitively obvious considering the two and three event examples given above.

Take an element x that is contained in r of the events. The $P(A_i)$ terms will contribute a $rP(x)$ factor to the

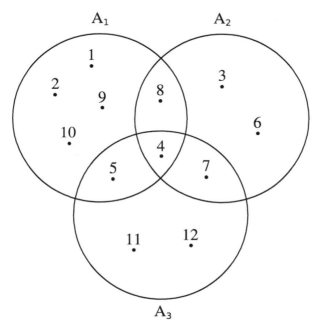

Figure 2: Three set example.

sum. The $P(A_i \cap A_j)$ terms contribute a $\binom{r}{2} P(x)$ factor, the $P(A_i \cap A_j \cap A_k)$ terms contribute a $\binom{r}{3} P(x)$ factor and so on. The part of the summation due to x is then equal to:

$$\left(\binom{r}{1} - \binom{r}{2} + \binom{r}{3} - \cdots - (-1)^r \binom{r}{r} \right) P(x) \quad (42)$$

You can see that the term multiplying $P(x)$ is always equal to 1 by comparing it to the expansion of $1 - (y - 1)^r$

$$1 - (y-1)^r \quad = 1 - y^r + \binom{r}{1} y^{r-1} - \binom{r}{2} y^{r-2}$$
$$+ \binom{r}{3} y^{r-3} - \cdots - (-1)^r \binom{r}{r} \quad (43)$$

Setting $y = 1$ shows that the term is always equal to 1 and so x only adds its probability once to the sum in equation 41.

In this book, a Bayesian problem is where we have one or more hypotheses and some evidence that determines how probable each hypothesis is. Take rolling dice for example. Suppose we know that a series of rolls was produced by either a set of fair or loaded dice but we don't know which. The hypothesis could be that the fair dice were used and the evidence is the result of the rolls.

Let H represent the hypothesis and E the evidence, then in a Bayesian problem we want to find the probability of the hypothesis given the evidence. This is written as the conditional probability, $P(H|E)$ (see Review of Discrete Probability). Using equation 7, this can be related to the probability of the evidence given the hypothesis as follows: $P(H|E)P(E) = P(E|H)P(H)$. If you solve for $P(H|E)$ you get an equation that is usually referred to as Bayes' theorem:

$$P(H|E) = \frac{P(E|H)P(H)}{P(E)} \qquad (44)$$

We could also ask for the probability that the hypothesis is false given the evidence. Let $\overline{H}$ represent the negation of the hypothesis, i.e. that the hypothesis is false, then we get a similar equation:

$$P(\overline{H}|E) = \frac{P(E|\overline{H})P(\overline{H})}{P(E)} \qquad (45)$$

Since the hypothesis is either true or false, we must have: $P(H|E) + P(\overline{H}|E) = 1$. Using this equation and the above two equations for $P(H|E)$ and $P(\overline{H}|E)$, we find:

$$P(E) = P(E|H)P(H) + P(E|\overline{H})P(\overline{H}) \qquad (46)$$

An example will show how all this works. Suppose we have two identical boxes. We know that one box contains 10 balls numbered 1 to 10 and the other contains 100 balls numbered 1 to 100. To determine which box is which, we are allowed to remove one ball from one of the boxes. We randomly choose a box and remove a ball which turns out to have the number 7. What is the probability that the box we chose is the one with 10 balls? Let the hypothesis be that we chose the box with 10 balls. The evidence is that the removed ball has the number 7. We will use equation 44 to calculate the probability of the hypothesis given the evidence. The term $P(H)$ is called the prior probability of the hypothesis. It is the probability before we have the evidence. Since the box was randomly chosen, it is equally likely to be the 10 or 100 ball box, therefore $P(H) = 1/2$. The probability that the 10 ball box was not chosen is $P(\overline{H}) = 1/2$. The term $P(E|H)$ in equation 44 is called the likelihood function. It is the probability of the evidence given that the hypothesis is true. In this case it is the probability of removing the 7 ball given that we chose the 10 ball box. Removing any one of the balls in the 10 ball box is equally likely so the probability is $P(E|H) = 1/10$. The probability of removing the 7 ball given that the 100 ball box was chosen is $P(E|\overline{H}) = 1/100$. Using equation 46 we can calculate $P(E) = (1/10)(1/2) + (1/100)(1/2) = 11/200$. Substituting all these values into equation 44, we get the probability the 10 ball box was chosen, given that the 7 ball was removed.

$$P(H|E) = \frac{(1/10)(1/2)}{11/200} = 10/11 \qquad (47)$$

This is called the posterior probability of the hypothesis. The probability has gone from $1/2$ before the evidence to $10/11$ after, or from fifty to over ninety percent.

This methodology can easily be extended to cases where there are several hypotheses, of which only one can be true. Suppose that in the above example we have three boxes instead of two. The three boxes have 10, 100, and 1000 balls and the removed ball could be from any one of them. Let A, B, and C be hypotheses that the ball was removed from the 10, 100, and 1000 ball boxes respectively, then their probabilities given the evidence are:

$$P(A|E) = \frac{P(E|A)P(A)}{P(E)} \qquad (48)$$

$$P(B|E) = \frac{P(E|B)P(B)}{P(E)} \qquad (49)$$

$$P(C|E) = \frac{P(E|C)P(C)}{P(E)} \qquad (50)$$

With $P(E)$ given by:

$$P(E) = P(E|A)P(A) + P(E|B)P(B) + P(E|C)P(C) \qquad (51)$$

The prior probabilities are all equal, $P(A) = P(B) = P(C) = 1/3$. The likelihoods are $P(E|A) = 1/10$, $P(E|B) = 1/100$, and $P(E|C) = 1/1000$. The evidence probability is $P(E) = (1/10+1/100+1/1000)(1/3) = 37/1000$. The posterior probabilities are then $P(A|E) = 100/111$, $P(B|E) = 10/111$, and $P(C|E) = 1/111$.

In the same manner you can extend this to four, five, or any number of hypotheses. The only restriction is that only one hypothesis can be true and one of the hypotheses must be true.

Most collection problems can be modeled in terms of putting balls into boxes. Suppose for example that a fast food restaurant is selling children's meals with a collectible toy inside. If there are a total of five different toys, how many meals do you have to buy to collect all the toys? Assume there is a random toy in each meal and all toys are equally likely. Let each of the five toys correspond to a box and the meals correspond to balls. Buying a meal is then equivalent to randomly placing a ball into a box. The question of how many meals are needed to collect all the toys, becomes the question of how many balls need to be randomly put into the boxes, so that there is at least one ball in each box. Another example is the question of how many times you need to roll a die to get all six faces at least once. In this case the faces correspond to boxes and a roll equates to randomly placing a ball in one of the boxes. In what follows we will show how to calculate probabilities related to randomly putting balls into boxes. We also calculate the average number of balls needed to get at least one in every box.

First let's find the probability that when r balls are randomly put into n boxes, all the boxes will contain at least one ball, i.e. there are no empty boxes. Obviously for this to be possible there must be at least as many balls as boxes, i.e. we must have $r \geq n$. When $r = n$

there are $n!$ ways the balls can be placed one to a box and n^n ways they can be placed without restriction so the probability is $n!/n^n$. Even for relatively small values of n, this is a small probability. For example in the case of rolling a die we have $n = 6$ so the probability that in six rolls of the die each face turns up once is $6!/6^6 = 5/324 = 0.0154321$.

For $r > n$ it is easier to first calculate the probability that at least one of the boxes is empty. Let A_i be the event that box i is empty in which case the r balls must be distributed into the remaining $n-1$ boxes. This can be done in $(n-1)^r$ ways so the probability is $P(A_i) = (n-1)^r/n^r = (1-1/n)^r$. The event $A_i \cap A_j$ indicates box i and j are empty and the r balls are distributed in the remaining $n-2$ boxes in $(n-2)^r$ ways so the probability is $P(A_i \cap A_j) = (1-2/n)^r$. In general, the event that k boxes are empty has probability $(1-k/n)^r$ and there are $\binom{n}{k}$ ways to have k out of n boxes empty. Using these probabilities in equation 41, we have for the probability that at least one of the boxes is empty:

$$P(A_1 \cup A_2 \cup \cdots A_n) = \sum_{k=1}^{n} (-1)^{k-1} \binom{n}{k} (1-k/n)^r \quad (52)$$

Subtract this probability from 1 and you have the probability that no box remains empty:

$$p_0(n, r) = \sum_{k=0}^{n} (-1)^k \binom{n}{k} (1-k/n)^r \quad (53)$$

Now we look at the probability of having exactly m empty boxes after randomly putting r balls into n boxes. The m empty boxes can be chosen in $\binom{n}{m}$ ways and for each choice of empty boxes, the balls can be distributed into the remaining $n-m$ boxes in $(n-m)^r p_0(n,r)$ ways such that none of them are empty. The total number of ways to have m empty boxes is then $\binom{n}{m}(n-m)^r p_0(n,r)$. To get the probability divide this by n^r.

$$p_m(n,r) = \binom{n}{m}(1 - \frac{m}{n})^r p_0(n,r) \qquad (54)$$

This can be simplified to:

$$p_m(n,r) = \binom{n}{m}\sum_{k=0}^{n-m}(-1)^k \binom{n-m}{k}\left(1 - \frac{m+k}{n}\right)^r$$

$$(55)$$

To find the average number of balls needed to get at least one ball in each box, define a set of random variables, X_k, that represent the number of balls needed to occupy a new box once k boxes already have balls in them. Obviously $X_0 = 1$ and the total number of balls needed to get at least one in each of the n boxes is

$$N = 1 + X_1 + X_2 + \cdots + X_{n-1} \qquad (56)$$

The average number of balls needed is then

$$E[N] = 1 + E[X_1] + E[X_2] + \cdots + E[X_{n-1}] \qquad (57)$$

so we just need to find the averages for the X_k variables. This turns out to be easy since each X_k variable is a geometric random variable. To see this, remember that a ball has an equal chance of landing in any of the n boxes, therefore the chance that it lands in one of the k boxes that already have balls is $q_k = k/n$ and the chance that it lands in an empty box is $p_k = 1 - q_k = 1 - k/n$. The probability that $X_k = m$ is then $q_k^{m-1} p_k$ which is the probability distribution for a geometric random variable. The expectation is

$$E[X_k] = \frac{1}{p_k} = \frac{n}{n-k} \tag{58}$$

and the expectation in equation 57 becomes

$$E[N] = 1 + \frac{n}{n-1} + \frac{n}{n-2} + \cdots + \frac{n}{1} \tag{59}$$

This simplifies to $E[N] = nH_n$ where H_n is called the nth harmonic number, defined as:

$$H_n = \sum_{k=1}^{n} \frac{1}{k} \tag{60}$$

The simplest example of a run is flipping a coin and getting a series of consecutive heads. Another example is rolling a die and getting a series of consecutive sixes. In both cases we have a sequence of actions and a result that occurs with probability p. If the result occurs r times in succession we call it a run of length r. The following discussion will talk about runs in terms of coin tosses but the results can be applied to other situations like the die roll mentioned above.

One run statistic that can be calculated rather easily is the average number of times a coin must be tossed to get a run of length r, which we will represent as μ_r. It takes on average μ_{r-1} tosses to get $r-1$ consecutive heads. If the next toss is a head then there will be r consecutive heads, so $\mu_r = \mu_{r-1} + 1$ with probability p, the probability of heads. If the next toss is a tail then it will take on average, another μ_r tosses to get r consecutive heads so $\mu_r = \mu_{r-1} + 1 + \mu_r$ with probability $q = 1 - p$, the probability of tails. From these two simple observations we get the following recursion equation:

$$\mu_r = p(\mu_{r-1} + 1) + q(\mu_{r-1} + 1 + \mu_r) \qquad (61)$$

which simplifies to

$$p\mu_r = \mu_{r-1} + 1 \qquad (62)$$

39

Starting with $\mu_0 = 0$ you can iterate this equation to find that

$$\mu_r = \sum_{k=1}^{r} \frac{1}{p^k} \qquad (63)$$

The sum is a geometric series so the equation simplifies to

$$\mu_r = \frac{1 - p^r}{qp^r} \qquad (64)$$

For a fair coin $p = q = 1/2$ and the equation is simply $\mu_r = 2(2^r - 1)$. Getting a run of three heads with a fair coin takes on average $\mu_r = 2(2^3 - 1) = 14$ tosses.

Other statistics are not so easily calculated and we will just list two of them here (for details see coin toss reference). The variance for the number of tosses needed to get a run of length r is:

$$\sigma_r^2 = \frac{1}{(qp^r)^2} - \frac{2r+1}{qp^r} - \frac{p}{q^2} \qquad (65)$$

The average number of tosses needed to get a run of heads of length h or a run of tails of length t is:

$$\mu_{h,t} = \frac{(1 - p^h)(1 - q^t)}{p^h q + pq^t - p^h q^t} \qquad (66)$$

Finally we look at run probabilities. Let f_n be the probability that it takes n tosses to get a run of heads of length r. It is relatively easy to get a recurrence equation for f_n. The initial values are: $f_n = 0$ for

$n < r$ and $f_r = p^r$. Also $f_n = qp^r$ for $r < n \leq 2r$ since the last $r + 1$ tosses must be a tail followed by r heads and the first $n - r - 1$ tosses cannot have a run when $n \leq 2r$. A recurrence is found by looking at the ways the sequence leading up to the run can start. With probability qf_{n-1}, the first toss is a tail and the run occurs $n - 1$ tosses later. With probability pqf_{n-2} the first toss is a head followed by a tail and the run occurs $n - 2$ tosses later. There can be up to $r - 1$ initial heads followed by a tail with the run occurring $n - r$ tosses later. The probabilities must therefore be related as follows:

$$f_n = qf_{n-1} + pqf_{n-2} + \cdots + p^{r-1}qf_{n-r} \qquad (67)$$

Using the initial values given above, this equation can be iterated to get any f_n probability.

Problem 1. If the probability of Skeeter winning a race against Sparky is 2/5, what is the probability of him not winning?

Answer. $1 - \frac{2}{5} = \frac{3}{5} = 0.6$

Problem 2. If the probability of rain today is 70%, what is the probability of it not raining?

Answer. Percentage in this case is just probability scaled by 100, so the probability of it not raining is $100\% - 70\% = 30\%$.

Problem 3. If the probability of Sparky hitting a target with a paint ball is 31/60, what is the probability of him missing?

Answer. $1 - \frac{31}{60} = \frac{29}{60}$.

Problem 4. If Spike, Spud, Skeeter, Sparky, and Spanky are competing in a race, with Spike's probability of winning being 1/6 and Spud's probability of winning 1/8, what is the probability that neither of them will win?

Answer. The sum of everyone's probability of winning must equal 1, therefore the probability that someone other than Spike and Spud wins is $1 - \frac{1}{6} - \frac{1}{8} = 1 - \frac{7}{24} = \frac{17}{24}$.

Problem 5. In a potato eating contest the odds are 10 to 1 in favor of Spud eating more potatoes than Spike. What is the probability that Spike will pull off an upset and win the contest?

Answer. Odds are a way to express a ratio of probabilities. Let p be the probability that some event occurs, then odds of a to b in favor means that $\frac{p}{1-p} = \frac{a}{b}$ or $p = \frac{a}{a+b}$. Likewise odds of a to b against means that $\frac{1-p}{p} = \frac{a}{b}$ or $p = \frac{b}{a+b}$. In the potato eating contest, the odds are $a = 10$ to $b = 1$ in favor of Spud so his probability of winning is $p = \frac{10}{11}$ and the probability of Spike winning is $1 - p = \frac{1}{11}$.

Problem 6. If the odds are 5 to 2 in favor of the Denver Broncos beating the San Diego Chargers, what are the probabilities of the Broncos winning and losing?

Answer. For a definition of odds, see the answer to the previous question. The odds are $a = 5$ to $b = 2$ in favor of the Broncos winning so the probability of winning is $p = \frac{5}{7}$ and the probability of losing is $1 - p = \frac{2}{7}$.

Problem 7. There are about 300 billion stars in the Milky Way Galaxy, with an average of one planet per star. If the odds of life on any randomly chosen planet are 1000 to 1 against, how many planets on average contain life?

Answer. The probability of life on any randomly chosen planet is $\frac{1}{1000+1} = \frac{1}{1001}$. So the average number of planets that contain life is then $300 \times 10^9 \left(\frac{1}{1001}\right) = 299,700,299.7$ or about 300 million planets.

Problem 8. What is the probability of a year, which is not a leap year, having 53 Sundays?

Answer. The number of weeks in a year is 52, which consists of $52 \cdot 7 = 364$ days. The remaining day in the year can be any day of the week, with equal probability. So the probability of 53 Sundays in a non-leap year is $1/7 = 0.1429$.

Problem 9. What is the probability that a randomly selected leap year contains 53 Sundays?

Answer. For a leap year, there are 2 days left over, following the 52 weeks. The 2 days are always contiguous, and can be any of the following with equal probability:

1. Sunday, Monday

2. Monday, Tuesday

3. Tuesday, Wednesday

4. Wednesday, Thursday

5. Thursday, Friday

6. Friday, Saturday

7. Saturday, Sunday

There are 7 possibilities, with 2 of them containing Sundays. So the probability of a randomly selected leap year containing 53 Sundays is $2/7 = 0.2857$.

Problem 10. If a leap year is any year divisible by 4, what's the probability that a year that's not the last year in a century (centuries start at 01 and go to 00) is a leap year?

Answer. Without the last year in a century, there are 99 years to choose from, with 24 of them being leap years. So the probability is $24/99 = 8/33 = 0.2424$.

Problem 11. A group of 10 people are randomly seated around a circular table. If Spike and Spud are in the group what is the probability that they end up seated together?

Answer. The number of unique circular arrangements of n objects is $(n-1)!$. There are two ways that Spike and Spud can be seated together, either Spud is to the right of Spike or Spike is to the right of Spud. In both cases they can be treated as a single unit and arranged with the 8 other people in 8! ways. The probability is then $2 \cdot 8!/9! = 2/9$.

Problem 12. A group of 23 knights randomly take their seats at the Round Table. Show that the odds are 10 to 1 against Sir Hector sitting next to Sir Bleoboris.

Answer. There are $(23-1)! = 22!$ unique ways that the knights can be seated around the table. Both when Bleoboris is seated to Hector's left and to his right there are $(22-1)! = 21!$ ways to seat the knights. The probability they sit together is then $p = 2 \cdot 21!/22! = 1/11$ and the odds against them sitting together are $\frac{a}{b} = \frac{10/11}{1/11} = \frac{10}{1}$ or 10 to 1.

Problem 13. A group of 10 people are randomly placed in a line. If Spike and Spud are in the group what is the probability that they end up next to each other?

Answer. Spike can either end up to the right of Spud or Spud can end up to the right of Spike. In either case they can be treated as a single unit and permuted with the others in 9! ways. The total ways that 10 people can be arranged is 10! so the probability is $2 \cdot 9!/10! = 1/5$.

Problem 14. An urn contains 5 black, 3 red, and 2 white balls. If we randomly select 3 balls from the urn, what is the probability of getting 2 black and one red ball?

Answer. There are $\binom{10}{3} = 120$ ways to select 3 balls from 10. Two black balls can be selected in $\binom{5}{2} = 10$ ways, and one red ball can be selected in 3 ways. So the probability of getting 2 black and one red ball is $\frac{10 \cdot 3}{120} = \frac{1}{4} = 0.25$.

Problem 15. If you randomly select four numbers from the integers 1 through 30, what is the probability that the numbers 1 and 2 will be among them?

Answer. Four numbers can selected from 30 in $\binom{30}{4} = 27405$ ways. The number of ways of getting 1 and 2 among the four selected numbers is $\binom{28}{2} = 378$. So the probability of getting 1 and 2 among the four is $378/27405 = 2/145 = 0.01379$, and the odds are 143 to 2 against getting both 1 and 2.

Problem 16. Sparky bought 3 tickets in a lottery with 3 ways to win and 6 ways to lose. Skeeter bought

1 ticket in a lottery with 1 way to win and 2 ways to lose. Show that Sparky has a better chance of winning than Skeeter, by a ratio of 16 to 7.

Answer. Sparky can buy 3 tickets out of 9 in $\binom{9}{3} = 84$ ways. He can lose in $\binom{6}{3} = 20$ ways. So his probability of winning is $1 - \frac{20}{84} = \frac{16}{21}$. Skeeter can buy a ticket in 3 ways, with his probability of winning being $\frac{1}{3}$. The ratio of Sparky's chances to Skeeter's is $\frac{16 \cdot 3}{21} = \frac{16}{7}$.

Problem 17. Powerball is a lottery that randomly draws 5 white balls from a drum of 59 balls labeled 1 to 59, and one red ball from a drum of 35 balls labeled 1 to 35. The jackpot is won by matching all white balls in any order, as well as the red ball. What are the odds of winning the jackpot?

Answer. There are 35 ways to choose the red ball, and $\binom{59}{5}$ ways to choose the 5 white balls. The number of possible tickets is then $35 \cdot \binom{59}{5} = 35 \cdot 5006386 = 175,223,510$. So the odds of winning the jackpot are about 1 in 175 million.

Problem 18. In the Colorado Lotto game, 6 numbers in the range of 1 to 42 are drawn. They are then sorted from lowest to highest and displayed on the lottery website. What's the probability there are at least 2 consecutive numbers? at least 3 consecutive numbers?

Answer. The total number of unique tickets for this game is $\binom{42}{6}$. Considering 2 consecutive numbers to be a block taken from the sorted list of numbers from 1 to 42, there are 41 blocks to choose from. The remaining 4 numbers can be chosen from the 40 that are left, which can be done in $\binom{40}{4}$ ways. So the probability of having at least 2 consecutive numbers is

$$\frac{41\binom{40}{4}}{\binom{42}{6}} = \frac{5}{7} = 0.7143$$

Similarly, the probability of having at least 3 consecutive numbers is

$$\frac{40\binom{39}{3}}{\binom{42}{6}} = \frac{20}{287} = 0.06969$$

Note that these probabilities include the possibility of having more than 2 consecutive, and 3 consecutive numbers, respectively.

Problem 19. A letter is randomly selected from the word *organize*, what is the probability that it is a vowel?

Answer. There are 8 letters of which 4 are vowels so the probability is $4/8 = 1/2$.

Problem 20. A letter is randomly selected from the word *resplendence*. What is the probability that the letter is e and what is the probability that it is n?

Answer. The letter e appears 4 times and the letter n appears twice. There are a total of 12 letters so the probability for e is $4/12 = 1/3$ and the probability for n is $2/12 = 1/6$.

Problem 21. If a letter is randomly selected from the word *paraphrase* what is the probability that it is a vowel and given that it is a vowel what is the probability that it is an a?

Answer. There are 10 letters and 4 vowels so the probability of selecting a vowel is $4/10 = 2/5$. Three of the 4 vowels are a's so given that a vowel was selected the probability of it being an a is $3/4$.

Problem 22. Two letters are randomly selected from the word *esteemed*. Show that the probability of not selecting two e's is the same as the probability of selecting at least one.

Answer. Replace every letter not equal to e with x then there are just as many x's as e's. Getting at least one e is the same as not getting two x's so the probability of getting at least one e is the same as the probability of not getting two x's.

Since there are just as many e's as x's, the probability of not getting two e's is the same as the probability of not getting two x's.

Problem 23. If two letters are randomly selected from the word *murmurer* what is the probability that they are equal?

Answer. The number of ways to select 2 letters from 8 is $\binom{8}{2} = \frac{8 \cdot 7}{2} = 28$. Out of these 28 selections there will be one *mm*, one *uu*, and three *rr* selections for a total of 5 selections with the letters equal so the probability is 5/28.

Problem 24. Two letters are randomly selected from the word *obsequious*. What is the probability that they are both vowels?

Answer. There are $\binom{10}{2} = \frac{10 \cdot 9}{2} = 45$ ways to select 2 letters from the 10. There are $\binom{6}{2} = \frac{6 \cdot 5}{2} = 15$ ways to select 2 vowels from the 6 so the probability is $15/45 = 1/3$.

Problem 25. Three letters are randomly selected from the word *association*. What is the probability that one of the letters is c?

Answer. There are $\binom{11}{3} = 165$ ways to select 3 letters and there are $\binom{10}{3} = 120$ ways to select 3 letters without the letter c, The probability of getting a c is then $1 - 120/165 = 3/11$.

Problem 26. Randomly select 3 letters from the word *association*. What is the probability that at least one of the letters is an s?

Answer. The number of ways to select 3 letters is $\binom{11}{3} = 165$. Without the two s's the number of ways to select is $\binom{9}{3} = 84$. The probability of getting at least one s is then $1 - 84/165 = 27/55$.

Problem 27. Three letters are randomly selected from the word *association*. What is the probability that 2 of the 3 letters are alike?

Answer. The number of ways to select 3 letters is $\binom{11}{3} = 165$. If 2 a's are selected then there are 9 ways to select the third letter. Similarly there are 9 ways to select 2 s's, o's, and i's so there are $4 \cdot 9 = 36$ selections with 2 letters alike. The probability is then $36/165 = 12/55$.

Problem 28. Randomly select 3 letters from the word *association*. What is the probability that only one of the letters is an s?

Answer. The number of ways to select 3 letters is $\binom{11}{3} = 165$. One s can be chosen in 2 ways and the remaining 2 letters can be chosen in $\binom{9}{2} = 36$ ways so the probability is $2 \cdot 36/165 = 24/55$.

Problem 29. Randomly arrange the letters of the word *obsequious*. Find the probability that all the vowels are grouped in a single block.

Answer. Some of the letters are alike but for this question we can treat them as 6 distinguishable vowels and 4 distinguishable consonants. If you take the 6 vowels as a single block then they can be arranged with the 4 consonants in $5! = 120$ ways. There are $6! = 720$ ways the vowels can be arranged within the block so there are $5! \cdot 6! = 86400$ arrangements with the the vowels in a single block. The total number of arrangements is $10!$ so the probability is $5! \cdot 6!/10! = 1/42$.

Problem 30. The letters of the word *oiseau* (french word for bird) are randomly arranged. What is the probability that the vowels are in alphabetical order?

Answer. There are 5 vowels and they can have $5! = 120$ possible arrangements only one of which will be in alphabetical order so the probability is $1/120$. Note that the one consonant can be positioned in just as many ways in the alphabetical arrangement as in each of the possible arrangements, so it is irrelevant.

Problem 31. One letter is chosen at random from the word *assistant* and one is chosen from the word *statistics*. What is the probability that the two letters are the same?

Answer. The possible double letters are *asit* and the number of ways to get them are $2 \cdot 1 = 2$ for *aa*, $3 \cdot 3 = 9$ for *ss*, $1 \cdot 2 = 2$ for *ii*, $2 \cdot 3 = 6$ for *tt*. The total number of ways to chose 2 letters is $9 \cdot 10 = 90$ so the probability is $(2+9+2+6)/90 = 19/90$.

Problem 32. One letter is chosen at random from the word *effete* and one is chosen from the word *feet*. What is the probability that the two letters are not the same?

Answer. Any of the letters *eft* can appear double, *ee* in $3 \cdot 2 = 6$ ways, *ff* in $2 \cdot 1 = 2$ ways, and *tt* in $1 \cdot 1 = 1$ way. The total number of ways to chose 2 letters is $6 \cdot 4 = 24$ so the probability of getting 2 letters the same is $(6 + 2 + 1)/24 = 3/8$ and the probability of getting them not the same is $1 - 3/8 = 5/8$.

Problem 33. If you place the 4 letters *sent*, in a row at random, what is the probability they form an English word?

Answer. There are $4! = 24$ possible permutations of the 4 letters, each equally likely to occur. There

are 4 possible English words from these permutations: *sent*, *nets*, *nest*, and *tens*. So the probability of forming an English word is $4/24 = 1/6 =$
0.1667.

Problem 34. Two letters are chosen at random from
the word *cocoa* and two are chosen from the word
cocoon. What is the probability that all four letters are different?

Answer. There are only 2 ways all four letters can
be different. The first is to choose *ca* from *cocoa* with probability $2/\binom{5}{2} = 1/5$ and choose *on*
from *cocoon* with probability $3/\binom{6}{2} = 1/5$. The
second is to choose *oa* from *cocoa* with probability $2/\binom{5}{2} = 1/5$ and choose *cn* from *cocoon* with
probability $2/\binom{6}{2} = 2/15$. So the probability is
$(1/5)(1/5) + (1/5)(2/15) = 1/15$

Problem 35. The letters of the word *replete* are randomly arranged. What is the probability that no
two *e*'s are side by side?

Answer. The four letters *rplt* can be arranged in $4! =$
24 ways. For each of these arrangements there are
5 places before, between or after the letters where
the 3 *e*'s can go. This means there are $\binom{5}{3} = 10$
ways to place the *e*'s and a total of $24 \cdot 10 = 240$
arrangements with no *e*'s side by side. The 7

letters can be arranged in a total of $7!/3! = 840$ ways so the probability is $240/840 = 2/7$.

Problem 36. The letters of the word *replete* are randomly arranged. What is the probability that all the e's are grouped together?

Answer. Treat the group of 3 e's as a single letter, then they can be arranged with the other 4 letters in $5! = 120$ ways. All 7 letters can be arranged in $7!/3! = 840$ ways, so the probability is $120/840 = 1/7$.

Problem 37. Solve the previous two problems if the arrangement of the letters is circular.

Answer. In general there are $(n - 1)!$ different circular arrangements of n distinct letters. There are $6!/3! = 120$ circular arrangements of the letters *replete* since there are 3 identical e's. The 4 letters *rplt* have $3! = 6$ circular arrangements and there are 4 places between letters in each arrangement. To keep the 3 e's apart they can be put into these places in 4 ways so the total number of circular arrangements with the e's apart is $6 \cdot 4 = 24$. The probability of a circular arrangement with the e's apart is then $24/120 = 1/5$. Treating the group of 3 e's as a single letter, there are $4! = 24$ circular arrangements and the probability of an arrangement with all the e's grouped together is once again $24/120 = 1/5$.

Problem 38. Randomly select 3 letters from *muhammadan*. What is the probability that all the letters are different?

Answer. The letters *ma* both appear 3 times while the remaining letters *uhdn* appear only once so you can select *ma* and one of the other letters in $3 \cdot 3 \cdot 4 = 36$ ways, you can select *m* or *a* and two of the other letters in $2 \cdot 3\binom{4}{2} = 36$ ways, and you can select 3 of the letters *uhdn* in $\binom{4}{3} = 4$ ways. The total ways of selecting 3 letters from the 10 is $\binom{10}{3} = 120$ so the probability is $(36 + 36 + 4)/120 = 76/120 = 19/30$.

Problem 39. Solve the previous problem with 5 randomly selected letters.

Answer. You can select *ma* and 3 of the other letters in $3 \cdot 3 \cdot 4 = 36$ ways, you can select *m* or *a* and all of the other letters in $2 \cdot 3 = 6$ ways. These are the only ways to select 5 letters with all of them different. The total ways to select 5 letters from 10 is $\binom{10}{5} = 252$. The probability is then $(36 + 6)/252 = 42/252 = 1/6$.

Problem 40. If 2 letters are randomly drawn from an alphabet of 20 consonants and 6 vowels, what is the probability that both letters are vowels?

Answer. The probability that the first letter is a vowel is $\frac{6}{26}$. The probability that the second letter is a vowel, given that the first also was, is $\frac{5}{25}$. So the probability that both letters are vowels is $\frac{6}{26} \cdot \frac{5}{25} = \frac{3}{65} = 0.04615$.

Problem 41. If you randomly take one domino from a set that goes from double blank to double 12, what is the probability you will get a domino with a 12?

Answer. Each half of a domino can have one of 13 items in it: blank, $1, 2, \ldots 11, 12$. The total number of dominoes in a set that goes from double blank to double 12 is the triangular number, $\sum_{i=1}^{13} i = 91$. There are 13 dominoes with a 12 on them, since the other numbers can range from blank to 12. So the probability of getting a domino with a 12 is $13/91 = 1/7 = 0.1429$.

Problem 42. A chess board is an 8 by 8 grid of squares. If 3 squares are randomly chosen on the board, what is the probability that they lie on the same line, excluding diagonal lines?

Answer. There are 16 lines (8 rows + 8 columns) with each line 8 squares long. Three randomly chosen squares in a line of 8 can be arranged in $\binom{8}{3}$ ways. Three squares on an 8 by 8 grid can be chosen in $\binom{64}{3}$ ways. So the probability they lie on the same line, excluding diagonals is

$$\frac{16\binom{8}{3}}{\binom{64}{3}} = \frac{16 \cdot 56}{41664} = \frac{896}{41664} = \frac{2}{93}$$
$$= 0.02151$$

Problem 43. For the previous problem, what is the probability that the 3 randomly chosen squares lie on a diagonal line?

Answer. There are 2 diagonal lines of length 8 squares, and 4 diagonal lines each of length 3, 4, 5, 6, and 7 squares. So the probability the randomly chosen squares lie on a diagonal line is

$$\frac{2\binom{8}{3} + 4\left[\binom{3}{3} + \binom{4}{3} + \binom{5}{3} + \binom{6}{3} + \binom{7}{3}\right]}{\binom{64}{3}}$$
$$= \frac{2 \cdot 56 + 4 \cdot 70}{41664} = \frac{392}{41664} = \frac{7}{744}$$
$$= 0.009409$$

Problem 44. Choose a random letter from the word *tinsel* and from the word *silent*. What is the probability that the two letters are the same?

Answer. Both words are composed of the same 6 unique letters so there are 6 ways to have a pair of the same letters. There are a total of 6^2 possible pairs of letters so the probability is $6/6^2 = 1/6$.

Problem 45. A random letter is chosen from the word *tinsel* and from the word *silent*. You are told that the two letters are of the same type, i.e. they are both vowels or both consonants. What is the probability that they are the same letter?

Answer. This is like the previous question but now there is the additional piece of information that the letters are of the same type, vowels or consonants. It can be solved as a conditional probability problem but we will simply look at it combinatorially. There are 4 consonants and 2 vowels so the number of pairs of the same type is $4^2 + 2^2 = 20$ and in only 6 of these pairs will the letters be the same. The probability is therefore $6/20 = 3/10$. The probability has almost doubled from $1/6$ to $3/10$ given the new information.

Problem 46. Two dice are thrown. What is the probability that the two numbers are equal? How does the probability change if you are told that the two numbers have the same parity (they are both even or both odd)?

Answer. There are 6 ways the two numbers can be equal and $6^2 = 36$ possible pairs of numbers so the probability of being equal is $6/6^2 = 1/6$. If the numbers have the same parity then they must both belong either to the set $1, 3, 5$ or the set $2, 4, 6$. The number of possible pairs is then $3^2 + 3^2 = 18$ and in 6 of these the numbers are equal, so the probability is $6/18 = 1/3$. Knowing that the numbers have the same parity has doubled the chances they are equal.

Problem 47. Choose a random letter from the word *musical* and from the word *amusing*. What is the probability the two letters are the same?

Answer. Each word is composed of 7 unique letters and 5 letters are common to both words so there are $7^2 = 49$ possible pairs of which 5 will have the same letters. The probability is therefore $5/49$.

Problem 48. Choose a random letter from the word *choice* and from the word *chance*. What is the probability they are the same letters?

Answer. Both words have two *c*'s so there are 4 ways a pair of *c*'s can be chosen. Two more identical pairs can be chosen from the common *h* and *e* for a total of 6 possible identical pairs. The total number of pairs is 6^2 so the probability is $6/6^2 = 1/6$.

Problem 49. Choose 2 random letters from the word *myrrh* and from the word *merry*. What is the probability they are the same?

Answer. The letters both words have in common are *myrr* from which there are 2 ways to select *mr*, 2 ways to select *yr*, 1 way to select *my*, and 1 way to select *rr*. So there are 4 ways the two selected pairs can be *mr*, 4 ways they can be *yr*, 1 way the can be *my*, and 1 way they can be *rr* for a total of $4 + 4 + 1 + 1 = 10$ ways the selected pairs can be equal. The total number of ways two pairs can be selected is $\binom{5}{2}^2 = 100$ so the probability is $10/100 = 1/10$.

Problem 50. There are 120 marbles of which only one is white. If they are randomly arranged into a rectangular grid of 10 by 12 marbles, what is the probability that the white marble is on the outer edge of the grid? If the grid is changed to 8 by 15, does the probability increase or decrease?

Answer. For the 10 by 12 grid there are 40 marbles along the outer edge and each is equally likely to be the white marble so the probability is $40/120 = 1/3$. For the 8 by 15 grid there are 42 marbles along the outer edge so the probability increases.

Problem 51. The 26 letters of the alphabet are ran-

domly arranged in a circle with no 2 vowels together. What is the probability that a is next to
b?

Answer. The letter a is a vowel so it must have consonants on both sides. There are 20 consonants
so the probability of a particular consonant being
on the clockwise side of a is $1/20$ and the probability of it being on the counter clockwise side
is $1/20$. The probability of finding b next to a is
then $2/20 = 1/10$.

Problem 52. The 26 letters of the alphabet are randomly arranged in a row with no 2 vowels together. What is the probability that a is next to
b?

Answer. Since they cannot appear next to a, and thus
affect the placement of b, the 5 other vowels can
be ignored. There are 21! ways to order the a and
the 20 consonants. The b can appear next to a
in 2 ways, as ab or ba, and these can be arranged
with the remaining 19 consonants in 20! ways.
The probability is therefore $2 \cdot 20!/21! = 2/21$.

Problem 53. Spike spent the afternoon visiting three
junkyards and lost a screw driver in one of them.
He usually has a 25 percent chance of loosing a
tool in a junkyard. What is the probability that
he left it in the first, second or third junkyard?

Answer. The probability that he lost it in the first junkyard is $1/4 = 0.25$. To lose it in the second junkyard he cannot have lost it in the first so the probability is
$(3/4)(1/4) = 3/16 = 0.1875$. To lose it in the third junkyard he cannot have lost it in the first two so the probability is
$(3/4)(3/4)(1/4) = 9/64 = 0.140625$.

Problem 54. If 6 coins are tossed, what is the probability that only one of them will turn up heads?

Answer. The probability of heads is $\frac{1}{2}$ and the probability of tails is also $\frac{1}{2}$, so the probability that the first coin will turn up heads and the rest turn up tails is $\frac{1}{2} \cdot \frac{1}{2} \cdot \frac{1}{2} \cdot \frac{1}{2} \cdot \frac{1}{2} \cdot \frac{1}{2} = \frac{1}{64}$. The same result is gotten for the probability that the second coin turns up heads and the others tails, and so on. So the probability that only one of the 6 coins turns up heads is $\frac{1}{64} + \frac{1}{64} + \frac{1}{64} + \frac{1}{64} + \frac{1}{64} + \frac{1}{64} = \frac{6}{64} = \frac{3}{32} = 0.09375$.

Problem 55. If 6 coins are tossed, what is the probability that at least one of them will turn up heads?

Answer. The probability that all 6 coins will turn up tails is $\frac{1}{2} \cdot \frac{1}{2} \cdot \frac{1}{2} \cdot \frac{1}{2} \cdot \frac{1}{2} \cdot \frac{1}{2} = \frac{1}{64}$. The probability that this is not true, or in other words that at least one will turn up heads is then $1 - \frac{1}{64} = \frac{63}{64} = 0.9844$.

Problem 56. Spike, Spud, and Sparky all want the last hot dog on the grill. They decide to flip a coin to see who gets it. First Spike and Spud flip the coin and who ever wins flips with Sparky to see who wins the hot dog. Is this a fair way to decide?

Answer. Both Spike and Spud have to win 2 coin flips to get the hot dog while Sparky only has to win once. The probability of winning once is $1/2$ while the probability of winning twice is $1/4$ so Sparky has a definite advantage.

Problem 57. In regard to the last question, what is a fair way to decide who gets the hot dog?

Answer. With only a single coin, one way is to flip the coin twice. If it is a fair coin then all 4 possible results HH, HT, TH, TT have an equal probability of $1/4$. If the result is HH Spike gets the dog, if it's HT Spud gets it, and if it's TH Sparky gets it. If the result is TT then the coin must be flipped twice again.

Problem 58. Spike and Spud randomly form a line with 10 other people. What is the probability that exactly three people end up between them?

Answer. There are $10 \cdot 9 \cdot 8 = 720$ ordered ways to select 3 people from 10 and 2 ways to put Spike and Spud on the ends. Any one of these groups of 5 people can then be arranged with the remaining 7 in 8! ways. The total number of arrangements is 12! so the probability is $2 \cdot 720 \cdot 8!/12! = 4/33$.

Problem 59. What is the probability in the previous question if the people are arranged in a circle instead of a line?

Answer. As before, the number of groups of 5 people with Spike and Spud on the ends is $2 \cdot 720 = 1440$. The number of circular arrangements of one of these groups of 5 with the remaining 7 people is 7!. The total number of circular arrangements of 12 people is 11!, so the probability is $1440 \cdot 7!/11! = 2/11$.

Problem 60. Andy, Billy, Chuck, Donny, and Eddie are scheduled to speak at the annual meeting of the Broadhead Valley Science Club. They can speak in any order except that Billy has to come after Andy because his theory depends on Andy's observations of the sleeping habits of Goldfish. If the scheduling is otherwise random, what is the probability that Billy speaks immediately after Andy.

Answer. Without restrictions there are $5! = 120$ possible schedules and in half of these Andy speaks before Billy so the number of acceptable schedules is 60. The number of schedules that put Billy immediately after Andy is $4! = 24$ so the probability is $24/60 = 2/5$.

Problem 61. If two integers are randomly chosen, what is the probability that their sum is even?

Answer. For the sum to be even, both integers must be even or odd. A randomly chosen integer is even or odd with an equal probability of $1/2$. The probability that both integers are even is $(1/2)(1/2) = 1/4$, and the probability they are both odd is also $1/4$. The probability the sum is even is therefore $1/4 + 1/4 = 1/2$.

Problem 62. Three integers between 1 and n are randomly chosen. What is the probability that the sum of any two is greater than the third? What is the probability if n is allowed to be arbitrarily large?

Answer. Let $f(n)$ be the number of ways to pick three integers between 1 and n such the sum of any two is greater than the third, then $f(n) - f(n - 1)$ will be the number of ways where at least one of the integers is equal to n. All three integers can equal n in only one way. Two of the integers can equal n either as nnx, nxn, or xnn where x

ranges from 1 to $n-1$ so the number of ways this can happen is $3(n-1)$. One of the integers can equal n in 3 ways with the other two chosen from 1 to $n-1$ in $\binom{n-1}{2}$ ways so the number of ways this can happen is $3\binom{n-1}{2}$. The number of ways where at least one of the integers equals n is then

$$
\begin{aligned}
f(n) - f(n-1) &= 1 + 3(n-1) + 3\binom{n-1}{2} \\
&= 1 + 3\binom{n}{2}
\end{aligned}
$$

When $n = 1$ the only way to pick the three numbers is so that they all equal 1 therefore $f(1) = 1$. For $n = 2$, above equation gives $f(2) = f(1) + 4 = 5$. The five sets of integers in this case are $(1,1,1)$, $(1,2,2)$, $(2,1,2)$, $(2,2,1)$, and $(2,2,2)$. Continuing on gives $f(3) = f(2) + 10 = 15$, $f(4) = f(3) + 19 = 34$, and so on. In general by iterating the equation you can see that $f(n)$ for $n \geq 2$ must be given by

$$
f(n) = n + 3 \sum_{k=2}^{n} \binom{k}{2}
$$

The sum in this equation reduces to $\binom{n+1}{3}$. When this is substituted into the equation and the result simplified we get $f(n) = n(n^2+1)/2$. To get the probability we divide this by n^3, the total number of sets of three numbers. This gives:

$$p(n) = \frac{1}{2} + \frac{1}{2n^2}$$

When n is allowed to go to infinity the second term in this equation goes to zero and the probability is just $p(\infty) = 1/2$. The probability in this case is equivalent to tossing a fair coin.

Problem 63. Let $a \leq b \leq c$ be three randomly chosen integers from 1 to $2n+1$. What is the probability that they form an arithmetic progression, i.e. $b - a = c - b = x$ for some positive integer x?

Answer. The arithmetic progression would contain a total of $2x + 1$ numbers so x can range from 1 to n and there are a total of $2n + 1 - 2x$ positions where the progression can start. The number of possible progressions is then

$$\sum_{x=1}^{n} (2n + 1 - 2x)$$

The sum simplifies to just n^2. The total number of ways three integers can be chosen from n is n^3 so the probability they form an arithmetic progression is $n^2/n^3 = 1/n$.

Problem 64. There are 6 black balls and 1 red ball in a bag. Balls are randomly removed until the red ball appears. What is the expected (average) number of balls removed?

Answer. The probability of selecting the red ball first is $1/7$. The probability of selecting it second is $(6/7)(1/6) = 1/7$. The probability of selecting it third is $(6/7)(5/6)(1/5) = 1/7$. In general the probability is $1/7$ that ball 1,2,3,4,5,6,7 is red. The expected number of balls is therefore $(0 + 1 + 2 + 3 + 4 + 5 + 6)/7 = 21/7 = 3$.

Problem 65. There are 10 white balls in a bag with half of them numbered 0 and the other half numbered 1,2,3,4,5. Three balls are sampled with replacement. What is the probability that the numbers on the sampled balls sum to 10?

Answer. You can draw: 5,5,0 in 3 orders and 5 ways (5 balls are numbered 0), 5,4,1 in 6 orders, 5,3,2 in 6 orders, 4,4,2 in 3 orders, and 4,3,3 in 3 orders. Total drawings that sum to 10 is $3 \cdot 5 + 6 + 6 + 3 + 3 = 33$. Total possible drawings is $10^3 = 1000$ so the probability is $33/1000$.

Problem 66. What is the probability in the previous question if the balls are not sampled with replacement?

Answer. In this case only a drawing of 5,4,1 or 5,3,2 will sum to 10. The total number of possible drawings is $\binom{10}{3} = 120$ so the probability is $2/120 = 1/60$.

Problem 67. A bag contains a 5 dollar note, a 10 dollar note, and 6 pieces of blank paper. What is the expectation of someone allowed to draw out one item?

Answer. There are 8 pieces of paper, so the probability of drawing out one particular item is $\frac{1}{8}$. The expectation for drawing out one item is then the sum of the products of the results and their corresponding probabilities, which is $\frac{5}{8} + \frac{10}{8} = \frac{15}{8} = 1.875$ dollars. Note that the results for the blank pieces of paper are zero, so only two terms are summed.

Problem 68. What is the expectation for drawing a note from a bag containing a 10 dollar note, and seven one dollar notes?

Answer. There are 8 notes, so the probability of drawing out one particular note is $\frac{1}{8}$. The expectation for drawing out one note is then $\frac{10}{8} + 7 \cdot \frac{1}{8} = \frac{17}{8} = 2.125$ dollars.

Problem 69. What is the expectation for drawing 2 coins from a bag containing 4 silver dollars, and 4 quarters?

Answer. Two coins can be drawn in $\binom{8}{2} = 28$ ways. There are $\binom{4}{2} = 6$ ways to draw 2 silver dollars, $4 \cdot 4 = 16$ ways to draw one silver dollar and one quarter, and $\binom{4}{2} = 6$ ways to draw 2 quarters. The respective probabilities are then $\frac{6}{28}$, $\frac{16}{28}$, and $\frac{6}{28}$. The expectation can now be calculated as $2 \cdot \frac{6}{28} + \frac{5}{4} \cdot \frac{16}{28} + \frac{1}{2} \cdot \frac{6}{28} = \frac{5}{4} = 1.25$ dollars. Note that the expectation is one fourth the sum of all the coin values in the bag.

Problem 70. Sparky and Spanky are both working on the same homework problem. If the probability of Sparky solving it is $\frac{2}{3}$, and the probability of Spanky solving it is $\frac{5}{12}$, what is the probability that they will both be unable to solve it?

Answer. The probability of Sparky failing to solve it is $\frac{1}{3}$, and the probability of Spanky failing to solve it is $\frac{7}{12}$, so the probability of both being unable to solve it is $\frac{1}{3} \cdot \frac{7}{12} = \frac{7}{36} = 0.1944$.

Problem 71. What are the probabilities that one but not the other will solve it?

Answer. The probability that Sparky solves it is $\frac{2}{3}$, and the probability that Spanky doesn't solve it is $\frac{7}{12}$, so the probability that Sparky solves it while Spanky doesn't, is $\frac{2}{3} \cdot \frac{7}{12} = \frac{7}{18} = 0.3889$. The probability that Sparky doesn't solve it is $\frac{1}{3}$, and the probability that Spanky solves it is $\frac{5}{12}$, so the probability that Sparky doesn't solve it while Spanky does, is $\frac{1}{3} \cdot \frac{5}{12} = \frac{5}{36} = 0.1389$.

Problem 72. One bag contains 5 silver dollars and 4 quarters, while another bag contains 5 silver dollars and 3 quarters. If a bag is grabbed at random and a coin is drawn out, what's the probability it's a silver dollar?

Answer. The probability of grabbing the first bag is $\frac{1}{2}$, and the probability of drawing a silver dollar from it is $\frac{5}{9}$. Similarly, the probability of grabbing the second bag is $\frac{1}{2}$, and the probability of drawing a silver dollar from it is $\frac{5}{8}$. So the total probability is $\frac{1}{2} \cdot \frac{5}{9} + \frac{1}{2} \cdot \frac{5}{8} = \frac{85}{144} = 0.5903$.

Problem 73. What is the expected (average) value of the coin drawn in the last question?

Answer. From the last question, the probability of drawing a silver dollar is $\frac{85}{144}$. So the probability of drawing a quarter must be $1 - \frac{85}{144} = \frac{59}{144}$. In terms of dollars, the expected value of the drawn coin is $\frac{85}{144} \cdot 1 + \frac{59}{144} \cdot \frac{1}{4} = \frac{133}{192} = 0.6927$ dollars.

Problem 74. What would have been the probability if all the coins in the last problem were put in one bag, and what would have been the expectation?

Answer. With all the coins in one bag, there would be 10 silver dollars and 7 quarters. The probability of drawing a silver dollar is then $\frac{10}{17}$ and the probability of drawing a quarter is $\frac{7}{17}$. The expectation is $\frac{10}{17} \cdot 1 + \frac{7}{17} \cdot \frac{1}{4} = \frac{47}{68} = 0.6912$ dollars. Both the probability of drawing a silver dollar, and the expectation of the drawing, are in this case slightly less than with the coins in two separate bags.

Problem 75. There are 3 different mountain trails ending at an alpine lake, and a certain picture I have in mind is at one of them. The odds that it's at the lake I'm thinking of is 3 to 2, but if it's not there, it's equally likely to be at either of the others. If I describe the lake I want the picture taken at, asking Spike to go there for me, the odds he gets there are 2 to 1. What is the probability of me getting the picture I want?

Answer. The probability Spike gets to the lake I described is $\frac{2}{2+1} = \frac{2}{3}$, and the probability that the picture I want taken is there is $\frac{3}{3+2} = \frac{3}{5}$. So the probability of getting the picture at the described lake is $\frac{2}{3} \cdot \frac{3}{5} = \frac{6}{15}$. The probability he gets to a different lake than the one I described is $\frac{1}{3}$, and the probability that he gets the picture anyway is $\frac{1}{2} \cdot \frac{2}{5} = \frac{1}{5}$. So the probability of getting the desired picture at a lake not described is $\frac{1}{3} \cdot \frac{1}{5} = \frac{1}{15}$. Therefore the probability of getting the picture at all is $\frac{6}{15} + \frac{1}{15} = \frac{7}{15}$, giving odds of 8 to 7 against getting it.

Problem 76. There are two bags of 10 coins each. The first bag contains one silver dollar and 9 quarters. The second bag contains 10 quarters. Nine coins are removed from the first bag and put into the second. Then nine coins are removed from the second bag and put into the first. Spanky is offered one of the bags. Which should he choose?

Answer. Since both bags contain the same number of coins, the only criterion for choosing is the probability that the silver dollar is in the bag. If the silver dollar is in the second bag, then it must have been moved from the first bag, with a probability of $\frac{9}{10}$, and it must not have been moved back to the first bag, with a probability of $1 - \frac{9}{19} = \frac{10}{19}$. The probability the silver dollar is in the second bag is then $\frac{9}{10} \cdot \frac{10}{19} = \frac{9}{19}$. The probability it's in the first bag is therefore $1 - \frac{9}{19} = \frac{10}{19}$. So the first bag should be chosen since it has a higher probability of containing the silver dollar.

Problem 77. If there are 3 independent events with probabilities $\frac{2}{3}$, $\frac{3}{5}$, and $\frac{1}{2}$, what is the probability that at least one of them will happen?

Answer. At least one of them will happen if not all of them fail. The probability that all of them fail is $\frac{1}{3} \cdot \frac{2}{5} \cdot \frac{1}{2} = \frac{1}{15}$. So the probability that at least one of them will happen is $1 - \frac{1}{15} = \frac{14}{15}$.

Problem 78. If there are 3 independent events with probabilities $\frac{2}{3}$, $\frac{3}{5}$, and $\frac{1}{2}$, what is the probability that exactly one of them will happen?

Answer. The probability that only the first will happen is $\frac{2}{3} \cdot \frac{2}{5} \cdot \frac{1}{2} = \frac{2}{15}$. The probability that only the second will happen is $\frac{1}{3} \cdot \frac{3}{5} \cdot \frac{1}{2} = \frac{1}{10}$. And the probability that only the third will happen is $\frac{1}{3} \cdot \frac{2}{5} \cdot \frac{1}{2} = \frac{1}{15}$. The probability that exactly one of them will happen is then $\frac{2}{15} + \frac{1}{10} + \frac{1}{15} = \frac{9}{30} = \frac{3}{10}$.

Problem 79. If on average 9 mountain climbers out of 10 return safely to the trailhead, what's the probability that with 5 climbers out, at least 3 will return safely?

Answer. The probability any particular climber returns is $\frac{9}{10}$. The probability any particular 3 climbers return is $\left(\frac{9}{10}\right)^3$. The probability any particular 2 climbers don't return is $\left(\frac{1}{10}\right)^2$. The number of ways to arrange 3 identical items in 5 bins is $\binom{5}{3} = 10$. So the probability that with 5 climbers out, exactly 3 return safely is $\left(\frac{9}{10}\right)^3 \cdot \left(\frac{1}{10}\right)^2 \cdot 10 = \frac{729}{10000}$. Similarly, the probability that with 5 climbers out, exactly 4 return safely is $\left(\frac{9}{10}\right)^4 \cdot \frac{1}{10} \cdot \binom{5}{4} = \frac{6561}{100000} \cdot 5 = \frac{32805}{100000}$. And the probability that all 5 return safely is $\left(\frac{9}{10}\right)^5 = \frac{59049}{100000}$. The probability that at least 3 out of 5 will return is then the sum of the probabilities that exactly 3, 4 or 5 will return, which is $\frac{7290}{100000} + \frac{32805}{100000} + \frac{59049}{100000} = \frac{12393}{12500} = 0.9914$.

Problem 80. Spike and Spud play against each other in a game for which there can't be a tie, and on average Spike wins 3 games out of 5. What's the probability Spike wins at least 3 games out of the first 5?

Answer. The probability Spike wins exactly 3 games out of 5 is $\left(\frac{3}{5}\right)^3 \cdot \left(\frac{2}{5}\right)^2 \cdot \binom{5}{3} = \frac{216}{625}$. Similarly, the probability Spike wins exactly 4 games out of 5 is $\left(\frac{3}{5}\right)^4 \cdot \frac{2}{5} \cdot \binom{5}{4} = \frac{162}{625}$. Finally, the probability Spike wins exactly 5 games out of 5 is $\left(\frac{3}{5}\right)^5 \cdot \binom{5}{5} = \frac{243}{3125}$. The probability that Spike wins at least 3 out of 5 games is then the sum of the probabilities that exactly 3, 4 or 5 will be won by Spike, which is $\frac{216}{625} + \frac{162}{625} + \frac{243}{3125} = \frac{2133}{3125} = 0.6826$. So the odds are better than 2 to 1 for Spike.

Problem 81. A bag contains m one dollar bills, and n twenty dollar bills. Binky is allowed to draw bills one at a time until he's drawn p twenties. Show that his expectation for the number of dollars he draws is $20p + \frac{pm}{n+1}$ dollars.

Answer. Statistically speaking, we can say the m one dollar bills are uniformly divided by the n twenty dollar bills into $n+1$ groups of mean value $= \frac{m}{n+1}$ dollars. The expectation of how many dollars Binky must draw to get one twenty dollar bill is then $20 + \frac{m}{n+1}$. By the linearity property of expectation, the expectation of how many dollars Binky must draw to get p twenty dollar bills is then $20p + \frac{pm}{n+1}$ dollars.

Problem 82. For the last question, if Binky replaces every bill he draws, what is his expectation then?

Answer. The ratio of one dollar bills to twenty dollar bills remains m/n so for every twenty dollar bill that he draws he can expect to draw on average m/n one dollar bills. If he draws p twenty dollar bills, then he can expect to get pm/n one dollar bills for a total of $20p + \frac{pm}{n}$ dollars.

Problem 83. There are 5 white and 4 black balls in an urn. If you randomly pull one by one out, what is the probability the first will be white, the second black, and so on alternately?

Answer. The 9 balls can be drawn in 9! ways. The 5 white balls can be arranged in their alternate positions in 5! ways, while the 4 black balls can similarly be arranged in 4! ways. So the probability is $\frac{5! \cdot 4!}{9!} = \frac{1}{126} = 0.007937$ meaning the odds are 125 to 1 against it. An equivalent way of looking at this problem is that there are $\binom{9}{5}$ ways that the nine balls can be pulled out of the bag. In only one of these ways do the colors alternate starting with white so the probability is $1/\binom{9}{5}$ which is the same as above.

Problem 84. In an urn are 5 red balls, 7 white balls, 4 green balls, and 3 black balls. If you randomly pull one by one out, what is the probability that first all the red balls will be removed, then all the white balls, then all the green, and finally all the black balls?

Answer. There are a total of 19 balls and the number of ways they can be pulled out of the bag is $\frac{19!}{5! \cdot 7! \cdot 4! \cdot 3!} = 1396755360$. Each of these ways is equally likely including pulling them out in the order described. There is only one way to pull them out in the order described so the probability is $\frac{1}{1396755360} = 7.159 \times 10^{-10}$.

Problem 85. From an urn containing 12 balls, 5 are drawn and replaced, and then 6 more are drawn. What is the probability that exactly 3 balls were common to the two drawings?

Answer. The second drawing can be made in $\binom{12}{6} = 924$ ways. Three of the balls can be drawn from the five in the first drawing in $\binom{5}{3} = 10$ ways. The other 3 balls can be drawn from the $12 - 5 = 7$ balls not in the first drawing in $\binom{7}{3} = 35$ ways. So the probability is $\frac{10 \cdot 35}{924} = \frac{25}{66} = 0.3788$.

Problem 86. A game involves tossing a coin 6 times or until a tail appears, which ever comes first. If the first toss is a head you receive 1 dollar and if it is a tail you receive nothing. Each subsequent toss that comes up heads doubles the amount you receive. If for example you toss 4 heads and then a tail, you will end up with 8 dollars. If all 6 tosses are heads then you receive 32 dollars. What is the average amount you receive?

Answer. The possible ending amounts are 0,1,2,4,8,16,32 with corresponding probabilities $1/2, 1/2^2, 1/2^3, 1/2^4, 1/2^5, 1/2^6, 1/2^6$ so the expectation is $1/2^2 + 2/2^3 + 4/2^4 + 8/2^5 + 16/2^6 + 32/2^6 = 7/4$.

Problem 87. When Spike and Spud play chess, Spike wins two thirds of the time. If you ignore possible draws, what is the probability that Spike wins 4 out of 6 games?

Answer. The probability of Spike winning any particular game is $2/3$ and the number of ways he can win 4 out of 6 games is $\binom{6}{4}$ so the probability is $\binom{6}{4}(2/3)^4(1/2)^2 = 80/243$.

Problem 88. Fat Freddies Pizza serves 4 kinds of pizza: possum, rabbit, crawdad and frog leg. On a scale of 1 to 10, Spike, Spud, and Sparky rate the four pizzas 10, 8, 8, and 6 respectively. If their probability of ordering a particular pizza is proportional to the rating what is the probability that they all order the same pizza?

Answer. The probabilities for the pizzas must be $10/32 = 5/16$, $8/32 = 1/4$, $8/32 = 1/4$, and $6/32 = 3/16$ so the probability they all order the same is $(5/16)^3 + (1/4)^3 + (1/4)^3 + (3/16)^3 = 35/512 = 0.068359$.

Problem 89. In the previous question what is the probability they all order different pizzas?

Answer. There are $\binom{4}{3} = 4$ groups of 3 different pizzas and then $3! = 6$ ways each group can be ordered. The probability of the 4 groups is $(5/16)(1/4)^2$, $(5/16)(1/4)(3/16)$, $(5/16)(1/4)(3/16)$, and $(1/4)^2(3/16)$. Summing these probabilities and multiplying by 6 gives $93/256 = 0.36328$. They are over 5 times more likely to order different pizzas than to order the same.

Problem 90. If you throw a single fair die 6 times, what is the probability that each of the numbers 1 through 6 will show up?

Answer. There are 6! ways the numbers 1 through 6 can be selected. The number of possible results from throwing a single die 6 times is 6^6. So the probability is $\frac{6!}{6^6} = \frac{720}{46656} = 0.01543$. The odds are about 200 to 3 against it.

Problem 91. When 2 dice are thrown, what is the probability that the sum will be greater than 8?

Answer. Out of the $6 \cdot 6 = 36$ ways the dice can fall, there are 10 ways they can sum to more than 8:

3 and 6, 4 and 5, 4 and 6, 5 and 6, 5 and 5,
6 and 3, 5 and 4, 6 and 4, 6 and 5, 6 and 6.

Problem 92. With 2 dice, what is the probability of throwing at least one ace (=1)?

Answer. There are three ways of getting at least one ace. The first die can be an ace and the second something else, with a probability of $\frac{1}{6} \cdot \frac{5}{6} = \frac{5}{36}$. The first die can be something else and the second die an ace, with a probability of $\frac{5}{6} \cdot \frac{1}{6} = \frac{5}{36}$. Finally, both dice can be an ace, with a probability of $\frac{1}{6} \cdot \frac{1}{6} = \frac{1}{36}$. The total probability is the sum of these three $= \frac{5}{36} + \frac{5}{36} + \frac{1}{36} = \frac{11}{36} = 0.3056$.

Problem 93. What is the probability of throwing 2 dice and getting neither an ace nor a six?

Answer. There are four ways of getting neither an ace nor a six on the first die, with a probability of $\frac{4}{6}$. There are four ways of getting neither an ace nor a six on the second die, with a probability of $\frac{4}{6}$. The total probability is the product of these two probabilities $= \frac{4}{6} \cdot \frac{4}{6} = \frac{16}{36} = \frac{4}{9} = 0.4444$.

Problem 94. With 2 dice, what are the odds against throwing doubles?

Answer. Out of the 36 ways the dice can fall, there are 6 ways to get doubles. So the probability of getting doubles is $\frac{6}{36} = \frac{1}{6}$, with the odds being therefore 5 to 1 against.

Problem 95. What is the probability of throwing 2 dice and getting neither an ace nor doubles?

Answer. The probability of not getting an ace on the first die is $\frac{5}{6}$. The probability of not getting an ace nor a double on the second die is $\frac{4}{6}$. The total probability is then the product of these two probabilities $= \frac{5}{6} \cdot \frac{4}{6} = \frac{20}{36} = \frac{5}{9} = 0.5556$.

Problem 96. With 2 dice, what is the probability of getting exactly eleven?

Answer. Out of the 36 ways the dice can fall, there are 2 ways (5 and 6, 6 and 5) to get exactly eleven. So the probability is $\frac{2}{36} = \frac{1}{18} = 0.05556$.

Problem 97. With 2 dice, what are all the possible sums and their probabilities? What is the most likely sum?

Answer. The sums of 2 dice can range from 2 to 12. The ways of getting these sums is listed below.

- 2: (1,1)
- 3: (1,2) (2,1)
- 4: (1,3) (3,1) (2,2)
- 5: (1,4) (4,1) (2,3) (3,2)
- 6: (1,5) (5,1) (2,4) (4,2) (3,3)
- 7: (1,6) (6,1) (2,5) (5,2) (3,4) (4,3)
- 8: (2,6) (6,2) (3,5) (5,3) (4,4)
- 9: (3,6) (6,3) (4,5) (5,4)
- 10: (4,6) (6,4) (5,5)
- 11: (5,6) (6,5)
- 12: (6,6)

There is one way to get the sums 2 and 12, so they each have probability $\frac{1}{36} = 0.02778$. There are 2 ways to get the sums 3 and 11, so they each have probability $\frac{2}{36} = \frac{1}{18} = 0.05556$. Similarly, sums 4 and 10 each have probability $\frac{3}{36} = \frac{1}{12} = 0.08333$. Sums 5 and 9 each have probability $\frac{4}{36} = \frac{1}{9} = 0.1111$. Sums 6 and 8 have probability $\frac{5}{36} = 0.1389$. Finally, sum 7 has probability $\frac{6}{36} = \frac{1}{6} = 0.1667$. So 7 is the most likely sum. The odds are 5 to 1 against getting a 7. All the probabilities are summarized below.

- Sums 2 and 12: $\frac{1}{36} = 0.02778$
- Sums 3 and 11: $\frac{2}{36} = 0.05556$
- Sums 4 and 10: $\frac{3}{36} = 0.08333$
- Sums 5 and 9: $\frac{4}{36} = 0.1111$
- Sums 6 and 8: $\frac{5}{36} = 0.1389$
- Sum 7: $\frac{6}{36} = 0.1667$

Problem 98. Compare the probabilities of throwing 4 with one die, 8 with two dice, and 12 with three dice, with two throws in each case.

Answer. The probability of throwing a 4 with one die is $\frac{1}{6}$. Throwing an 8 with two dice can be done by throwing (4,4), (3,5), and (2,6). The ways of doing this is 1, 2, and 2 respectively. So the probability of throwing 8 with two dice is $\frac{1+2+2}{6^2} = \frac{5}{36}$. Throwing a 12 with three dice can be done in the ways shown in table 1. So the probability of throwing 12 with three dice is $\frac{1+6+6+6+3+3}{6^3} = \frac{25}{216}$. The probability of not getting a 4 with one die is

Dice	Ways
4,4,4	1
4,5,3	6
4,6,2	6
5,6,1	6
3,3,6	3
5,5,2	3

Table 1: Ways to throw 12 with 3 dice, for problem 98.

$\frac{5}{6}$, and with two throws is $\left(\frac{5}{6}\right)^2$, so the probability of getting a 4 with one die in two throws is $1 - \left(\frac{5}{6}\right)^2 = \frac{11}{36}$. The probability of not getting an 8 with two dice is $\frac{31}{36}$, and with two throws is $\left(\frac{31}{36}\right)^2$, so the probability of getting an 8 with two dice in two throws is $1 - \left(\frac{31}{36}\right)^2 = \frac{335}{1296}$. The probability of not getting a 12 with three dice is $\frac{191}{216}$, and with two throws is $\left(\frac{191}{216}\right)^2$, so the probability of getting a 12 with three dice in two throws is $1 - \left(\frac{191}{216}\right)^2 = \frac{10175}{46656}$. Now to compare the probabilities with 1, 2, and 3 dice respectively:

$$\frac{11}{36} : \frac{335}{1296} : \frac{10175}{46656}$$

Forming common denominators, then removing the denominator, we get:

$$14256 : 12060 : 10175$$

So getting a 4 with one die in two throws is most

likely, and getting a 12 with 3 dice in two throws is least likely.

Problem 99. What's the probability of throwing not more than 8 with a single throw of three dice?

Answer. First let's determine the number of ways to throw not more than 8 with a single throw of 3 dice. This is the number of ways you can place 3, 4, 5, 6, 7, and 8 identical balls into 3 distinct bins with at least one ball in each bin. From eq. 38 in Review of Basic Combinatorics the number of ways you can place n identical balls into m distinct bins with at least one ball in each bin is $\binom{n-1}{m-1}$. So the number of ways here is

$$\sum_{k=3}^{8} \binom{k-1}{3-1} = 56$$

The probability of throwing not more than 8 with a single throw of 3 dice is then $\frac{56}{6^3} = \frac{7}{27} = 0.2593$.

Problem 100. If 3 dice are thrown, what are the probabilities that they will all be the same, only 2 the same, or all different?

Answer. The probability that the second die is the same as the first is $\frac{1}{6}$, and the probability that the third die is the same as the first is also $\frac{1}{6}$. So the probability that all 3 are the same is $\frac{1}{6} \cdot \frac{1}{6} = \frac{1}{36}$. The probability that the second die is the same as the first is $\frac{1}{6}$, while the probability that the third die is different is $\frac{5}{6}$. There are $\binom{3}{2} = 3$ ways for only 2 dice to be the same, so the probability that only 2 dice are the same is $\frac{1}{6} \cdot \frac{5}{6} \cdot 3 = \frac{15}{36}$. The probability that the 3 dice are all different is $\frac{5}{6} \cdot \frac{4}{6} = \frac{20}{36}$. So the respective probabilities are $\frac{1}{36}$, $\frac{15}{36}$, and $\frac{20}{36}$. These probabilities add up to 1, since there is no other way the dice can fall.

Problem 101. Spud throws 3 dice, and wins 6 dollars if they all turn up alike, 4 dollars if only two turn up alike, and 3 dollars if they are all different. What is his expectation?

Answer. Using the probabilities from the previous question, the expectation is $6 \cdot \frac{1}{36} + 4 \cdot \frac{15}{36} + 3 \cdot \frac{20}{36} = \frac{7}{2} = 3.5$ dollars, or 3 dollars and 50 cents.

Problem 102. Spike continues to throw a single die until he gets an ace. What's the probability he needs to throw it at least 10 times? What's the probability he needs to throw it exactly 10 times?

Answer. The probability of not getting an ace in 9 throws is $\left(\frac{5}{6}\right)^9 = \frac{1953125}{10077696} = 0.1938$. So the probability Spike needs to throw at least 10 times for an ace is 0.1938. The probability Spike needs to throw exactly 10 times is $\left(\frac{5}{6}\right)^9 \cdot \frac{1}{6} = \frac{1953125}{60466176} = 0.03230$.

Problem 103. Alex, Bruce, Carol, and Dotty will each throw a die in order. The first one to throw an ace gets a prize. What are their respective probabilities and what's the probability that none of them will win?

Answer. Alex goes first, so his probability of winning is $\frac{1}{6} = 0.1667$. Bruce is second, and can only win if Alex loses, so Bruce's probability of winning is $\frac{5}{6} \cdot \frac{1}{6} = \frac{5}{36} = 0.1389$. Carol is third and can only win if Alex and Bruce both lose, so her probability of winning is $\frac{5}{6} \cdot \frac{5}{6} \cdot \frac{1}{6} = \frac{25}{216} = 0.1157$. Dotty is last and can only win if the 3 others all lose, so her probability of winning is $\frac{5}{6} \cdot \frac{5}{6} \cdot \frac{5}{6} \cdot \frac{1}{6} = \frac{125}{1296} = 0.09645$. Similarly, the probability of none of them winning is $\frac{5}{6} \cdot \frac{5}{6} \cdot \frac{5}{6} \cdot \frac{5}{6} = \frac{625}{1296} = 0.4823$. Note that the sum of these probabilities $\frac{1}{6} + \frac{5}{36} + \frac{25}{216} + \frac{125}{1296} + \frac{625}{1296} = 1$, because there are no other possibilities.

Problem 104. Sparky and Spanky alternately throw a single die until whoever throws the first ace gets one dollar. If Sparky goes first, what are their expectations?

Answer. The probability of winning

- at the 1st throw is $\frac{1}{6}$
- at the 2nd throw is $\frac{1}{6} \cdot \frac{5}{6}$
- at the 3rd throw is $\frac{1}{6} \cdot \left(\frac{5}{6}\right)^2$
- at the 4th throw is $\frac{1}{6} \cdot \left(\frac{5}{6}\right)^3$
- at the 5th throw is $\frac{1}{6} \cdot \left(\frac{5}{6}\right)^4$
- at the 6th throw is $\frac{1}{6} \cdot \left(\frac{5}{6}\right)^5$

and so on. The 1st, 3rd, and 5th throws are Sparky's, so his probability of winning is:

$$\frac{1}{6} + \frac{1}{6} \cdot \left(\frac{5}{6}\right)^2 + \frac{1}{6} \cdot \left(\frac{5}{6}\right)^4 + \ldots$$

The 2nd, 4th, and 6th throws are Spanky's, so his probability of winning is:

$$\frac{1}{6} \cdot \frac{5}{6} + \frac{1}{6} \cdot \left(\frac{5}{6}\right)^3 + \frac{1}{6} \cdot \left(\frac{5}{6}\right)^5 + \ldots$$

Note that Spanky's probability is equal to Sparky's times $\frac{5}{6}$. The total prize is one dollar which must be the sum of the expectations. So Sparky's expectation must be $\frac{6}{11}$ of a dollar or 54.5 cents, while Spanky's expectation must be $\frac{5}{11}$ of a dollar or 45.5 cents.

Problem 105. If you throw 2 dice, what's the probability you'll get snake eyes (2 aces) exactly 4 times in 6 throws?

Answer. The probability of getting snake eyes on any throw is $\frac{1}{6} \cdot \frac{1}{6} = \frac{1}{36}$. The probability of not getting snake eyes is $\frac{5}{6} \cdot \frac{5}{6} = \frac{25}{36}$. The number of ways to arrange 4 identical items in 6 bins is $\binom{6}{4} = \frac{6 \cdot 5}{2} = 15$. So the probability of getting snake eyes exactly 4 times in 6 throws is $\left(\frac{1}{36}\right)^4 \cdot \left(\frac{25}{36}\right)^2 \cdot 15 = \frac{3125}{725594112} = 4.307 \times 10^{-6}$. So the odds are about a million to 4 against it.

Problem 106. If you throw 5 dice, what's the probability you'll get a triple and a double (known as a full house in the Milton Bradley game Yahtzee).

Answer. Five dice can be thrown in 6^5 ways. There are $\binom{6}{2} = 15$ possibilities for the 2 different triple and double numbers and the number of ways they can appear on the dice is $\frac{5!}{3!2!} = 10$. The number of ways to get a triple and a double is then $15 \cdot 10 = 150$ and the probability is $\frac{150}{6^6} = \frac{25}{7776} = 0.003215$.

Problem 107. In the game Chuck-a-Luck you place a one dollar bet on a number from 1 through 6, then throw 3 dice. If the number you bet on appears once, you get your dollar back. If it appears twice, you get back double your money, 2 dollars. If it appears 3 times, you get back 10 times your money, 10 dollars. Otherwise you lose. What are the probabilities of winning?

Answer. Three dice can be thrown in 6^3 ways. The number you bet on can appear once on 3 dice in $\binom{3}{1} = 3$ ways, while the number of ways it can appear is $1 \cdot 5 \cdot 5 = 25$. So the probability the number you bet on appears once is $\frac{3 \cdot 25}{6^3} = \frac{75}{216} = \frac{25}{72} = 0.3472$. The number you bet on can appear twice on 3 dice in $\binom{3}{2} = 3$ ways, while the number of ways it can appear is $1 \cdot 1 \cdot 5 = 5$. So the probability the number you bet on appears twice is $\frac{3 \cdot 5}{6^3} = \frac{15}{216} = \frac{5}{72} = 0.06944$. The number you bet on can appear 3 times on 3 dice in $\binom{3}{3} = 1$ way, while the number of ways it can appear is $1 \cdot 1 \cdot 1 = 1$. So the probability the number you bet on appears 3 times is $\frac{1 \cdot 1}{6^3} = \frac{1}{216} = 0.004630$. The probability of winning anything is then $\frac{25}{72} + \frac{5}{72} + \frac{1}{216} = \frac{91}{216} = 0.4213$.

Problem 108. What is the expectation for the Chuck-a-Luck game described in the previous question?

Answer. The expectation is the sum of the products of the payoffs times the probabilities: $\frac{25}{72} \cdot \$1 + \frac{5}{72} \cdot \$2 + \frac{1}{216} \cdot \$10 = \$0.5324$. So for every dollar you bet, you'll average a return of about 53 cents.

Problem 109. In the dice game Bunco, you throw 3 dice, and there are 6 rounds of dice throwing. In each round you earn points if the number of that round shows up on the dice throw. One point is earned if the number appears once, 2 points if it appears twice, and 21 points if it appears three times. If you throw 3 dice once, what is the probability you get one occurence of the designated number (1-6), 2 occurences, and 3 occurences?

Answer. One occurence of the designated number can happen in $\binom{3}{1} \cdot 1 \cdot 5 \cdot 5 = 3 \cdot 25 = 75$ ways. Two occurences can happen in $\binom{3}{2} \cdot 1 \cdot 1 \cdot 5 = 3 \cdot 5 = 15$ ways, and three occurences in $\binom{3}{3} \cdot 1 \cdot 1 \cdot 1 = 1$ way. The total possibilities in throwing 3 dice is $6^3 = 216$. So the probabilities are:

$$P(1 \text{ occurence}) = \frac{75}{6^3} = \frac{25}{72} = 0.3472$$

$$P(2 \text{ occurences}) = \frac{15}{6^3} = \frac{5}{72} = 0.06944$$

$$P(3 \text{ occurences}) = \frac{1}{6^3} = 0.004630$$

Problem 110. What is the expectation of Bunco, described in the previous question, in terms of points?

Answer. The expectation is the sum of the products of the points earned times the probabilities: $\frac{25}{72} \cdot$ 1pt $+ \frac{5}{72} \cdot$ 2pts $+ \frac{1}{216} \cdot$ 21pts $= 0.5833$ points. So every time you throw 3 dice in Bunco, you earn on average 0.5833 points.

Problem 111. Six dice are thrown one time. What is

the probability of getting a double and a quadruple?

Answer. There are $\binom{6}{2} = 15$ possibilities for the 2 different double and quadruple numbers, and the number of ways they can appear on the dice is $\frac{6!}{2!4!} = 15$. The number of ways to get a double and a quadruple is then $15 \cdot 15 = 225$ and the probability is $\frac{225}{6^6} = \frac{25}{5184} = 0.004823$.

Problem 112. A pair of dice are thrown twice in succession what is the probability that the pair of numbers on the second throw are the same as on the first?

Answer. There are 36 possible results for each throw and therefore 36 ways the 2 throws can be the same. The probability is therefore $36/36^2 = 1/36$.

Problem 113. In the previous question what is the probability that the two pairs of numbers will have at least one number in common?

Answer. It is easier to first calculate the probability that the two throws have no numbers in common. The outcomes on the dice for the second throw must be limited to 5 numbers each for there to be no numbers in common with the first throw. This means there are only 25 possibilities for the second throw. The probability of the two throws having no numbers in common is then $36 \cdot 25/36^2 = 25/36$. The probability that they have at least one number in common must then be $1 - 25/36 = 11/36$.

Problem 114. If two dice are rolled three times, what is the probability of getting a seven (sum of the two dice) at least twice?

Answer. The ways to get a seven are: $(6,1)$, $(1,6)$, $(5,2)$, $(2,5)$, $(4,3)$, $(3,4)$. There are 36 possible rolls of 2 dice so the probability of a seven is $6/36 = 1/6$. In 3 rolls there are 3 ways to get 2 sevens so the probability of 2 sevens is $3(1/6)^2(5/6)$. The probability of 3 sevens is $(1/6)^3$ and the probability of 2 or more sevens is $(15 + 1)/6^3 = 2/27$.

Problem 115. Spike and Spud take turns throwing 2 dice with Spike going first. Spike wins if he throws a 6 and Spud wins if he throws a 7. What are their win probabilities?

Answer. A 6 can be thrown in 5 ways: $(5,1)$, $(1,5)$, $(4,2)$, $(3,3)$, so the probability of throwing a 6 is $p = 5/36$. From the results of the previous question the probability of throwing a 7 is $q = 1/6$. Since Spike goes first, he can win on the first, third, fifth, ... throws. His probability of winning on the first throw is p. To win on the third throw he must lose on the first and Spud must lose on the second. This has probability $(1-p)(1-q)p$. His probability of winning on the fifth throw is $(1-p)^2(1-q)^2p$. The overall probability of winning is given by the sum of an infinite series.

$$p\sum_{k=0}^{\infty}(1-p)^k(1-q)^k = \frac{p}{1-(1-p)(1-q)}$$

Substituting the numbers into this gives a probability of 30/61 for Spike winning. The probability of Spud winning is $1-30/61 = 31/61$. Spud has a slight advantage.

Problem 116. Spike, Spud, and Sparky in order take turns throwing a single die. The first person to throw a 1 wins. What are their win probabilities?

Answer. The probability of throwing a 1 is $p = 1/6$ and the probability of not throwing a 1 is $q = 1-p = 5/6$. Spike can win on the first, fourth, seventh, etc. throws so his probability of winning is

$$p\sum_{k=0}^{\infty}q^{3k} = \frac{p}{1-q^3}$$

Likewise Spud's probability of winning is

$$pq\sum_{k=0}^{\infty}q^{3k} = \frac{pq}{1-q^3}$$

and Sparky's probability of winning is

$$pq^2 \sum_{k=0}^{\infty} q^{3k} = \frac{pq}{1-q^3}$$

Putting in the numbers gives probabilities of $36/91$, $30/91$, and $25/91$ for Spike, Spud, and Sparky.

Problem 117. Two faces of a die have even numbers and four have odd numbers. What is the probability that the sum of 4 throws is an even number.

Answer. For the sum to be even there can only be 0, 2, or 4 odd throws. The probability of an even number is $2/6 = 1/3$ and the probability of an odd number is $4/6 = 2/3$. The probability of the sum being even is then $(1/3)^4 + \binom{4}{2}(1/3)^2(2/3)^2 + (2/3)^4 = 41/81$.

Problem 118. Two dice are thrown. One of them is fair and the other is loaded in some arbitrary way. Show that the probability of getting a double with these dice is the same as the probability of getting a double with a pair of fair dice.

Answer. For the fair die, the probability of each of the faces is $1/6$. For the unfair die, let p_i be the probability of face i. The probability of getting a double is then $(p_1 + p_2 + p_3 + p_4 + p_5 + p_6)/6$. The p_i probabilities must sum to 1 so the probability of getting a double reduces to 1/6 which is the same as the probability with a pair of fair dice. Another way to look at this is that, whatever the number on the loaded die, the probability of getting the same number on the fair die is 1/6.

Problem 119. In the previous question let both of the dice be loaded in the same arbitrary way. Show that the probability of getting a double is now higher than for a pair of fair dice.

Answer. If p_i is the probability of face i for each of the dice then the probability of a double is $p_1^2 + p_2^2 + p_3^2 + p_4^2 + p_5^2 + p_6^2$. This is the equation for a paraboloid in six dimensions which has a minimum at the origin. But the p_i values are constrained to lie on the plane defined by $p_1 + p_2 + p_3 + p_4 + p_5 + p_6 = 1$. The point on this plane that is closest to the origin is where all the p_i values are equal to 1/6. Any movement away from this point will be a movement away from the origin which will increase the value of the paraboloid and the probability of a double.

Problem 120. Two dice are loaded in the same way but the chance of getting a double or seven is the same as with a pair of fair dice. Show that this is only possible if the sum of the probabilities of opposite faces is the same as for a fair die, i.e. $p_1 + p_6 = 1/3$, $p_2 + p_5 = 1/3$, and $p_3 + p_4 = 1/3$.

Answer. The probability of a seven is $2(p_1p_6 + p_2p_5 + p_3p_4)$ and the probability of a double is $p_1^2 + p_2^2 + p_3^2 + p_4^2 + p_5^2 + p_6^2$. If you add these probabilities and factor the result you get $(p_1 + p_6)^2 + (p_2 + p_5)^2 + (p_3 + p_4)^2$ as the probability of a double or seven. This is a paraboloid which, if the p_i values are constrained to add to 1, has a minimum when $p_1 + p_6 = 1/3$, $p_2 + p_5 = 1/3$, and $p_3 + p_4 = 1/3$.

Problem 121. When Spike goes fishing he has about a one percent chance of catching a big fish. On average, how many times does he have to go fishing to get a big one?

Answer. Geometric Distribution: Common sense says that if he has a one out of a hundred chance of catching a big fish then he needs to go fishing about 100 times to get a big one. We will prove that this is indeed the case. Let $p = 0.01$ be the probability that he catches a big fish on any particular trip and $q = 1 - p = 0.99$ be the probability that he does not. The probability that it takes him n trips to catch a big fish is then pq^{n-1}. This is called a geometric probability distribution. Let $E[n]$ be the average number of trips (the expectation of n) then by definition:

$$E[n] = p \sum_{n=1}^{\infty} nq^{n-1}$$

Let $f(q)$ represent the infinite sum which when written out is:

$$f(q) = 1 + 2q + 3q^2 + 4q^3 + \cdots$$

If $qf(q)$ is subtracted from $f(q)$ the result is:

$$f(q) - qf(q) = (1 - q)f(q) = 1 + q + q^2 + q^3 + \cdots$$

The right hand side of this equation is a geometric series that sums to:

$$1 + q + q^2 + q^3 + \cdots = \frac{1}{1 - q}$$

To see this, just multiply both sides of the equation by $1-q$. Putting this into the previous equation and solving for $f(q)$ gives

$$f(q) = \frac{1}{(1 - q)^2} = \frac{1}{p^2}$$

Using this in the equation for $E[n]$ gives

$$E[n] = \frac{p}{p^2} = \frac{1}{p}$$

for the average number of trips. Putting in the numbers we get $E[n] = 1/0.01 = 100$. Spike will have to go fishing about 100 times to get a big fish.

Problem 122. If a major meteorite impact occurs on the Earth an average of once every 100 years, what is the probability that five such meteorites will impact in the next 500 years?

Answer. There are a number of ways to model this problem. The simplest is to assume that the number of years to the next meteor impact is a geometric random variable (see previous problem) with a constant probability, p, of an impact in any given year. The probability that it takes n years for the next impact is then $p(1-p)^{n-1}$ and the average number of years between impacts is $1/p$. The problem states that the average number of years between impacts is 100 therefore $p = 1/100$. Five impacts in the next 500 years can happen in $\binom{500}{5}$ ways so the probability is $\binom{500}{5}p^5(1-p)^{495} = 0.176351$. This probability can be difficult to evaluate without a good computer algebra system. An alternative is to assume the number of impacts is given by a Poisson distribution (see one of the probability references). With a Poisson distribution the probability would be given by $\frac{\lambda^5 e^{-\lambda}}{5!}$ where $\lambda = np = 500/100 = 5$. This easily evaluates to 0.175467.

Problem 123. On average, how many times do you have to roll a die so that each face turns up at least once?

Answer. This is a collection problem where we are trying to collect all six faces of a die. We get the first face on the first roll. The probability of getting the next face is 5/6 and the number of rolls needed to get it is a geometric random variable with mean 6/5. Once we have the second face, the probability of getting the next is 4/6 and the mean number of rolls needed to get it is 6/4. In general, once k faces have been collected the probability of getting the next one is $p_k = (6 - k)/6$ and the mean number of rolls needed to get it is $1/p_k = 6/(6-k)$. Adding up the mean number of rolls needed for each new face gives

$$\frac{6}{6} + \frac{6}{5} + \frac{6}{4} + \frac{6}{3} + \frac{6}{2} + \frac{6}{1} = \frac{147}{10}$$

It will take on average about 15 rolls to get all six faces.

Problem 124. If $n \geq 6$ dice are thrown what is the probability that all six numbers appear at least once on the dice? How many dice do you have to throw for at least a 50 percent chance of having all the numbers show?

Answer. The number of possible results is 6^n. If $n = 6$ then there are 6! ways that all six numbers can appear so the probability is $6!/6^6 = 5/324 = 0.0154321$. For $n > 6$ it is easier to find the probability that at least one of the numbers is missing and then subtract this from 1. Let A_i be the event that number i is missing so the n dice are limited to the remaining 5 numbers in 5^n ways giving a probability of $P(A_i) = 5^n/6^n = (5/6)^n$. The probability that at least one of the numbers is missing is $P(A_1 \cup A_2 \cup \cdots A_6)$. But the events are not mutually exclusive, numbers i and j can both be missing, A_i and A_j can both occur. This means we cannot just sum the $P(A_i)$ probabilities. We have to calculate the probabilities for multiple missing numbers and then use the procedure outlined in nonexclusive probabilities. The event $A_i \cap A_j$ indicates numbers i and j are both missing, the n dice are limited to 4 numbers in 4^n ways and the probability is $P(A_i \cap A_j) = 4^n/6^n = (4/6)^n$. In general the event that k numbers are missing has probability $(6-k)^n/6^n = (1-k/6)^n$ and there are $\binom{6}{k}$ of these events. Using equation 41 in nonexclusive probabilities, the probability of at least one missing number is:

$$P(A_1 \cup A_2 \cup \cdots A_6) = \sum_{k=1}^{5}(-1)^{k-1}\binom{6}{k}(1-k/6)^n$$

Subtract this probability from 1 and you have the probability of no missing numbers:

$$p(n) = \sum_{k=0}^{5}(-1)^k\binom{6}{k}(1-k/6)^n$$

For various values of n we have

$$p(10) = 0.271812$$

$$p(11) = 0.356206$$
$$p(12) = 0.437816$$
$$p(13) = 0.513858$$
$$p(14) = 0.582845$$
$$p(15) = 0.644213$$

At least 13 dice have to be thrown for a greater than 50 percent chance of getting all the numbers.

Problem 125. A baseball player is batting 400 (he hits the ball 40 percent of the time). What is the probability that in the next 4 at bats he will hit the ball exactly twice?

Answer. Since he is batting 400 we can assume his probability of hitting the ball at any bat is $p = 0.4 = 2/5$. There are $\binom{4}{2} = 6$ ways he can hit twice in 4 tries so the probability is $6p^2(1-p)^2 = 216/625 = 0.3456$.

Problem 126. A football team wins at home games 60 percent of the time. What is the probability that in five at home games they win exactly 3 times?

Answer. Using only the given information, we have to assume that the probability of winning any particular at home game is $p = 0.6 = 3/5$. There are $\binom{5}{3} = 10$ ways they can win exactly 3 out of 5 at home games so the probability is $10p^3(1-p)^2 = 216/625 = 0.3456$.

Problem 127. In the previous question what is the probability the team wins at least 3 at home games?

Answer. The team can win 3 games in $\binom{5}{3} = 10$ ways, 4 games in 5 ways and 5 games in 1 way so the probability is $10p^3(1-p)^2 + 5p^4(1-p) + p^5 = 2133/3125 = 0.68256$. This is much higher than the probability of winning exactly 3 games.

Problem 128. A chess player wins 30 percent of the time, loses half the time, and plays to a draw 20 percent of the time. What is the probability that in the next 10 games he wins 3 times, loses 5 times, and draws twice.

Answer. The probabilities of winning, losing and drawing are $3/10$, $1/2$, and $1/5$ respectively. The number of ways to get 3 wins, 5 losses, and 2 draws in 10 games is $\frac{10!}{3!5!2!} = 2520$ so the probability is $2520(3/10)^3(1/2)^5(1/5)^2 = 1701/20000 = 0.08505$.

Problem 129. A basketball player makes twice as many free throws as he misses. What is the probability that he makes at least 4 of the next 6 free throws?

Answer. Making twice as many free throws as he misses means his probability of making a free throw must be $p = 2/3$ and his probability of missing is $q = 1 - p = 1/3$. He can make 4 out of 6 in $\binom{6}{4} = 15$ ways, 5 out of 6 in 6 ways and 6 out of 6 in 1 way so the probability is $15p^4p^2 + 6p^5q + p^6 = 496/729 = 0.680384$.

Problem 130. If 4 cards are taken from a well shuffled deck, what is the probability there will be one of each suit?

Answer. Four cards can be taken from the deck in $\binom{52}{4} = 270725$ ways. Four cards can be taken, with one from each suit in $13 \cdot 13 \cdot 13 \cdot 13 = 28561$ ways. So the probability is $\frac{28561}{270725} = 0.1055$, meaning the odds are about 10 to 1 against it.

Problem 131. If 4 cards are taken from a well shuffled deck, what is the probability they will be marked 2, 3, 4, 5?

Answer. Four cards can be taken from the deck in $\binom{52}{4} = 270725$ ways. There are 4 ways to choose each of the 4 specified cards. So the probability is $\frac{4 \cdot 4 \cdot 4 \cdot 4}{270725} = \frac{256}{270725} = 0.0009456$, meaning the odds are about 1000 to 1 against it.

Problem 132. If 5 cards are taken from a well shuffled deck, what is the probability they form a full house (3 matching cards of one rank, 2 matching cards of another rank)?

Answer. Five cards can be taken from the deck in $\binom{52}{5} = 2598960$ ways. The number of ways to get 3 matching cards of one rank is $13 \cdot \binom{4}{3} = 52$. The number of ways to get 2 matching cards of another rank is $12 \cdot \binom{4}{2} = 72$. Therefore the probability is $\frac{52 \cdot 72}{2598960} = \frac{3744}{2598960} = 0.001441$. So the odds are about 1000 to 1.

Problem 133. Sparky draws one card at a time from a well shuffled deck. He stops once he's drawn n hearts. Show that the expectation for the number of cards he must draw is $\frac{53}{14} \cdot n$ cards.

Answer. In a deck of cards, there are 13 hearts, and 39 non-hearts. Statistically speaking, we can say the 39 non-hearts are uniformly divided by the 13 hearts into 14 groups of mean length $= \frac{39}{14}$ cards. The expectation of how many cards Sparky must draw to get one heart is then $1 + \frac{39}{14} = \frac{53}{14}$. By the linearity property of expectation (see eq. 27 in Review of Discrete Probability), the expectation of how many cards Sparky must draw to get n hearts is then $\frac{53}{14} \cdot n$.

Problem 134. Skunk draws one card at a time from a well shuffled deck. He stops once he's drawn all 4 aces. What is the expectation for the number of cards he must draw?

Answer. A deck of cards has 48 non-aces. Statistically speaking, we can say the 48 non-aces are uniformly divided by the 4 aces into 5 groups of mean length $= \frac{48}{5}$ cards. The expectation of how many cards Skunk must draw to get one ace is then $1 + \frac{48}{5} = \frac{53}{5}$. By the linearity property of expectation, the expectation of how many cards Skunk must draw to get 4 aces is then $\frac{53}{5} \cdot 4 = \frac{212}{5} = 42.4$.

Problem 135. Rowdy draws cards one at a time from a well shuffled deck and replaces them until he gets 2 aces in a row. What's the expectation for the number of cards he will draw?

Answer. From eq. 64 of Solving Run Problems, the mean number of times, μ, required to get r successive repetitions of an event with probability p is

$$\mu = \frac{1 - p^r}{qp^r}$$

where $q = 1 - p$. In this case p is the probability of drawing an ace, which is $\frac{4}{52} = \frac{1}{13}$. $r = 2$, and $q = \frac{12}{13}$. The expectation for the number of cards required to draw 2 consecutive aces is then

$$
\begin{aligned}
\mu &= \frac{1 - \left(\frac{1}{13}\right)^2}{\left(\frac{12}{13}\right)\left(\frac{1}{13}\right)^2} \\
&= \frac{13^3 - 13}{12} = 182
\end{aligned}
$$

Problem 136. Weezy draws cards one at a time from a well shuffled deck and replaces them until he gets 4 spades in a row. What's the expectation for the number of cards he will draw?

Answer. As in the last problem, we use eq. 64 of Solving Run Problems for the mean number of times, μ, required to get r successive repetitions of an event with probability p, and $q = 1 - p$.

$$
\mu = \frac{1 - p^r}{qp^r}
$$

In this case p is the probability of drawing a spade which is $\frac{13}{52} = \frac{1}{4}$. $r = 4$, and $q = \frac{3}{4}$. The expectation for the number of cards required to draw 4 consecutive spades is then

$$
\begin{aligned}
\mu &= \frac{1 - \left(\frac{1}{4}\right)^4}{\left(\frac{3}{4}\right)\left(\frac{1}{4}\right)^4} \\
&= \frac{4^5 - 4}{3} = 340
\end{aligned}
$$

Problem 137. Skeeter throws a die until he's thrown two 6's in a row, and then gets a dollar for every 6 he's thrown. What's his expectation in dollars?

Answer. With the same formula used in the last question, the mean number of throws required to get two 6's in a row is

$$\mu = \frac{1 - \left(\frac{1}{6}\right)^2}{\left(\frac{5}{6}\right)\left(\frac{1}{6}\right)^2}$$
$$= \frac{6^3 - 6}{5} = 42$$

On the average, 42 throws will result in $42 \cdot \frac{1}{6} = 7$ sixes, so Skeeter's expectation is 7 dollars. Note that although Skeeter's last two throws are 6's, this fact has no effect on his expectation.

Problem 138. We have a set of four red cards to which we add two more cards. Each of the two added cards is equally likely to be red or black. Now the six cards are shuffled and three cards are dealt. What is the probability that all three cards are red.

Answer. The probability that the two added cards were both red or both black is $1/4$, and the probability that one was red and one was black is $2/4 = 1/2$. There are 3 possible compositions of the deck, it can have 0, 1 or 2 black cards with probabilities 1/4, 1/2, and 1/4 respectively. With an all red deck the probability of being dealt 3 red cards is 1. With one black card the probability is $\binom{5}{3}/\binom{6}{3} = 1/2$, and with two black cards the probability is $\binom{4}{3}/\binom{6}{3} = 1/5$. So the overall probability of being dealt 3 red cards is $(1/4)1 + (1/2)(1/2) + (1/4)(1/5) = 11/20$.

Problem 139. A box contains 8 envelopes. One of them contains $10, one contains $5 and the other 6 are empty. You are allowed to randomly remove envelopes one by one until you get one that is empty. How much money can you expect to collect?

Answer. Let T, F, and Z represent envelopes with ten, five, and zero dollars then the following drawing sequences will result in money: TZ or FZ both with probability $(1/8)(6/7) = 3/28$, TFZ or FTZ both with probability $(1/8)(1/7) = 1/56$. The expectation is then $10(3/28) + 5(3/28) + 15(1/56) + 15(1/56) = 15/7$.

Problem 140. Spike starts walking toward Purgatory 20 miles away at a constant speed between 3 and 4 miles/hour. He randomly chooses the speed using a uniform distribution from 3 to 4, i.e. his speed is equally likely to be any value in that range. An hour after he leaves Spud starts out after him at a constant speed of 4 miles/hour. Find the probability that Spud catches up with Spike.

Answer. At a constant speed of 4 miles/hour, Spud will take 5 hours to get to Purgatory. He leaves an hour after Spike so he will catch up to him only if Spike takes more than 6 hours. To take more than 6 hours, Spike must walk at a speed less than $20/6 = 10/3$ or three and one third miles/hour. Spike has the same probability for going any fractional amount over 3 miles/hour so the probability that he goes less than 3 and $1/3$ miles/hour must be $1/3$.

Problem 141. When Spike and Spud play chess Spike wins on average 5 games out of 9. If they play 3 games what is the probability of Spike winning the majority of the games?

Answer. We can assume the probability of Spike winning any particular game is $p = 5/9$. There is one way he can win all 3 games and 3 ways he can win 2 of the games so the probability is $p^3 + 3p^2(1 - p) = 425/729 = 0.58299$.

Problem 142. A basketball player is twice as likely to make his next shot if he made the previous one. If he makes a shot what is the probability he will make at least 2 out of the next 3 shots?

Answer. Making a shot means his probability of making the next shot is $p = 2/3$ and his probability of missing is $q = 1 - p = 1/3$. The probability of him making the next 3 shots is p^3. The probability of him making the next 2 shots and missing the third is $p^2 q$. The probability of him making the next shot, missing the second, and making the third is pq^2. This is also the probability of him missing the next shot and then making the next two. The probability of him making at least 2 of the 3 shots is then $p^3 + p^2 q + 2pq^2 = 16/27$.

Problem 143. Show that as long as the faces of two dice are numbered in the same way, not necessarily from 1 to 6, then the probability of rolling an even number (sum of the two dice) can never be less than 1/2.

Answer. Let a be the number of even numbers and b the number of odd numbers on each die. If the roll results in two even or two odd numbers then the sum will be even and there are $a^2 + b^2$ ways this can happen. If the roll results in one even and one odd number then the sum will be odd and there are $2ab$ ways this can happen. The probability of an even sum cannot be less than 1/2 as long as $a^2 + b^2 - 2ab \geq 0$ which can be written as $(a - b)^2 \geq 0$. The inequality is clearly true for any values of a and b. When $a = b$

the probability of rolling an even number will be exactly $1/2$.

Problem 144. A line randomly forms with n people. If Spike and Spud are in the line, what is the probability that r people stand between them?

Answer. Spike can be ahead of or behind Spud and they can have r people between them in $(n-2)!/(n-2-r)!$ ways. The group can be arranged with the remaining $n-2-r$ people in $(n-1-r)!$ ways. The number of unrestricted ways to form the line is $n!$ so the probability is $\frac{2(n-2)!(n-1-r)!}{(n-2-r)!n!} = \frac{2(n-1-r)}{n(n-1)}$.

Problem 145. In the previous question what is the probability if the people are randomly formed into a circle instead of a line?

Answer. Spike and Spud can form a line with r people between them in the same number of ways as before. The remaining $n-2-r$ people can be put into a circular arrangement with them in $(n-2-r)!$ ways. The number of unrestricted circular arrangements is $(n-1)!$ so the probability is $\frac{2(n-2)!(n-2-r)!}{(n-2-r)!(n-1)!} = \frac{2}{n-1}$. The probability is now independent of r.

Problem 146. There are m white and n black balls in a bag. If the balls are randomly removed from the bag one by one what is the probability that the colors alternate until only one color remains?

Answer. You can record the result of removing the balls one by one as an $m + n$ digit binary number with a 1 representing a white ball and a 0 representing a black ball. The number of $m + n$ digit binary numbers with m ones and n zeros is $\binom{m+n}{m}$. Only 2 of these binary numbers have alternating ones and zeros at the begining followed by all ones or all zeros. The probability is therefore $2/\binom{m+n}{m} = 2 \cdot m!n!/(m+n)!$.

Problem 147. In the previous problem what is the probability that all of one color is removed first?

Answer. Again there are only 2 ways this can happen so the probability is the same as before $2/\binom{m+n}{m} = 2 \cdot m!n!/(m+n)!$.

Problem 148. A box contains n each of m different kinds of donuts for a total of nm donuts. If r donuts are randomly taken from the box what is the probability that they are all different?

Answer. If $r > m$ then the probability is clearly zero so we will assume $r \leq m$. The total number of ways to select r donuts from nm is $\binom{nm}{r}$ since the order in which they are selected is irrelevant. The number of ways to select r kinds of donuts from m kinds is $\binom{m}{r}$ and for each kind there are n donuts to choose from, so the number of ways to get r different kinds of donuts is $\binom{m}{r}n^r$. The probability is then $\frac{\binom{m}{r}n^r}{\binom{nm}{r}}$.

Problem 149. When Spud reaches into a potato chip bag he pulls out either one or two chips with the same probability of $1/2$. After reaching into the bag $2n$ times what is the most likely number of chips that he's eaten.

Answer. Since pulling out one or two chips have equal probability, the most likely occurence is that he took one chip n times and two chips n for a total of $3n$ chips.

Problem 150. In the previous problem suppose Spud reaches into the bag 10 times, so $n = 5$. What is the probability that he eats exactly 15 chips and what is the probability that he eats between 13 and 17 chips?

Answer. Let a be the number of times he gets only 1 chip and b the number of times he gets 2 chips then $a + b = 2n$ and if he ends up with exactly k chips then $a + 2b = k$. Solving these equations for a and b gives $a = 4n - k$ and $b = k - 2n$. The probability that his $2n$ reaches into the bag result in 1 chip a times and 2 chips b times is then

$\binom{2n}{a}(1/2)^a(1/2)^b = \binom{2n}{b}(1/2)^{2n}$. Using $2n = 10$ this becomes $\binom{10}{k-10}(1/2)^{10}$ and for $k = 15$ the probability is $63/256 = 0.24609375$. The probability he eats between 13 and 17 chips is given by the sum

$$\sum_{k=13}^{17} \binom{10}{k-10}(1/2)^{10} = 57/64 = 0.890625$$

There is almost a 90 percent certainty that he ate between 13 and 17 chips.

Problem 151. Four dice are thrown one time. What is the probability of getting a single double?

Answer. The number for the double can be chosen in 6 ways. The other two numbers must be different from themselves and the double number so they can be chosen in $\binom{5}{2} = 10$ ways. The four numbers can appear on the dice in $4!/2! = 12$ ways so the number of ways to get a single double is $6 \cdot 10 \cdot 12 = 720$. The probability of a single double is then $720/6^4 = 5/9 = 0.5556$.

Problem 152. Four dice are thrown one time. What is the probability of getting two different doubles?

Answer. There are $\binom{6}{2} = 15$ possibilities for the two different double numbers and the number of ways they can appear on the dice is $\frac{4!}{2!2!} = 6$. The number of ways to get two doubles is then $15 \cdot 6 = 90$ and the probability is $90/6^4 = 5/72 = 0.06944$.

Problem 153. Six dice are thrown one time. What is the probability of getting three different doubles?

Answer. There are $\binom{6}{3} = 20$ possibilities for the three different double numbers and the number of ways they can appear on the dice is $\frac{6!}{2!2!2!} = 90$. The number of ways to get three doubles is then $20 \cdot 90 = 1800$ and the probability is $1800/6^6 = 25/648 = 0.03858$.

Problem 154. Six dice are thrown one time. What is the probability of getting two different triples?

Answer. There are $\binom{6}{2} = 15$ possibilities for the two different triple numbers and the number of ways they can appear on the dice is $\frac{6!}{3!3!} = 20$. The number of ways to get two triples is then $15 \cdot 20 = 300$ and the probability is $300/6^6 = 25/3888 = 0.00643$.

Problem 155. A bag contains 5 balls. There is an equal probability that the balls are either all black or all white. A white ball is put into the bag, and then a ball is randomly removed, which turns out to be white. What is the probability that the original 5 balls were all white?

Answer. This problem can be solved using Bayes' theorem. The hypothesis H, is that the original 5 balls were all white, and the evidence E, is that the removed ball is white. The prior probability of the hypothesis $P(H)$, is the probability that the original 5 balls were all white before the white ball was removed. The 5 balls were equally likely to be all black or all white, so the prior probability of the hypothesis is $P(H) = \frac{1}{2}$. It follows that the prior probability that the hypothesis is false is $P(\overline{H}) = \frac{1}{2}$. The likelihood of the evidence given the hypothesis is true is $P(E|H) = 1$ since if the original 5 balls were white, then there would be 6 white balls in the bag when one is removed. Similarly the likelihood of the evidence given the hypothesis is false is $P(E|\overline{H}) = \frac{1}{6}$. Now we can calculate the posterior probability of the hypothesis, given the evidence, using Bayes' theorem:

$$
\begin{aligned}
P(H|E) &= \frac{P(E|H)P(H)}{P(E|H)P(H) + P(E|\overline{H})P(\overline{H})} \\
&= \frac{1 \cdot \frac{1}{2}}{1 \cdot \frac{1}{2} + \frac{1}{6} \cdot \frac{1}{2}} \\
&= \frac{6}{7}
\end{aligned}
$$

The evidence has increased the probability that the original 5 balls were white from $\frac{1}{2}$ to $\frac{6}{7}$.

Problem 156. In a package of 1000 dice, one die is

marked 6 on every side. The others are marked as normal. If you randomly choose a die from the package and without inspecting it, throw it 4 times, each time getting a 6, what's the probability the die is the bad one?

Answer. Solving this with Bayes' theorem, the hypothesis H is that the randomly chosen die is the one marked 6 on every side, and the evidence E is that when the die is tossed 4 times, it comes up 6 every time. The prior probability of the hypothesis $P(H)$, is the probability that the randomly chosen die is the bad one before throwing it 4 times, so the prior probability of the hypothesis is $P(H) = \frac{1}{1000}$. It follows that the prior probability that the hypothesis is false is $P(\overline{H}) = \frac{999}{1000}$. The likelihood of the evidence given the hypothesis is true is $P(E|H) = 1$ since if the die is marked 6 on all sides, you're sure to throw four 6's in a row. Similarly the likelihood of the evidence given the hypothesis is false is $P(E|\overline{H}) = \left(\frac{1}{6}\right)^4$. Now we can calculate the posterior probability of the hypothesis, given the evidence, using Bayes' theorem:

$$P(H|E) = \frac{P(E|H)P(H)}{P(E|H)P(H) + P(E|\overline{H})P(\overline{H})}$$

$$= \frac{1 \cdot \frac{1}{1000}}{1 \cdot \frac{1}{1000} + \left(\frac{1}{6}\right)^4 \cdot \frac{999}{1000}}$$

$$= \frac{48}{85}$$

$$= 0.5647$$

The evidence has increased the probability that the randomly chosen die is bad from 0.001 to 0.5647.

Problem 157. A bag contains 10 coins, each of which could be a quarter or a silver dollar with equal probability. If a randomly chosen coin is pulled out of the bag and it's a silver dollar, what's the probability it was the only silver dollar in the bag?

Answer. We can solve this problem with Bayes' theorem. The hypothesis H, is that the bag contains one silver dollar and nine quarters gotten by a process of choosing 10 times with equal probability whether or not to put a silver dollar or a quarter in the bag. The evidence E is that a silver dollar was pulled out of the bag.
$P(H) = \frac{\binom{10}{1}}{2^{10}} = \frac{10}{2^{10}}$ and $P(\overline{H}) = \frac{2^{10}-10}{2^{10}}$

$$P(E|H) = \frac{1}{10}$$

$P(E|\overline{H})$ = prob. of evidence given H is not true.

= prob. we pull out dollar with 2 in bag

+ prob. we pull out dollar with 3 in bag

+ ...

+ prob. pull out dollar with 10 in bag

$$= \frac{2}{10} \cdot \frac{\binom{10}{2}}{2^{10}} + \frac{3}{10} \cdot \frac{\binom{10}{3}}{2^{10}} + \ldots + \frac{10}{10} \cdot \frac{\binom{10}{10}}{2^{10}}$$

$$= \frac{1}{10 \cdot 2^{10}} \sum_{k=2}^{10} k \binom{10}{k} = \frac{5110}{10 \cdot 2^{10}} = \frac{511}{2^{10}}$$

$$P(H|E) = \frac{P(E|H)P(H)}{P(E|H)P(H) + P(E|\overline{H})P(\overline{H})}$$

$$= \frac{\frac{1}{10} \cdot \frac{10}{2^{10}}}{\frac{1}{10} \cdot \frac{10}{2^{10}} + \frac{511}{2^{10}} \cdot \frac{2^{10}-10}{2^{10}}}$$

$$= \frac{1}{1 + \frac{511(2^{10}-10)}{2^{10}}}$$

$$= \frac{512}{259589} = 0.001972$$

So the odds are about 1000 to 2, or 500 to 1, against the silver dollar being the only one in the bag.

Problem 158. A bag contains 10 coins, which are either quarters or silver dollars, and all possible numbers of each are equally likely. If a randomly chosen coin is pulled out of the bag and it's a silver dollar, what's the probability it was the only silver dollar in the bag?

Answer. This problem appears to be identical to the last, but it's different because here the question doesn't specify that each coin in the bag could be one of 2 types with equal probability. In this case, the probability distribution for the composition of the bag is uniform, all compositions have the same probability. This was not the case in the previous problem. We can solve this problem also with Bayes' theorem. The hypothesis H, is that the bag contains one silver dollar and nine quarters. The evidence E is that a silver dollar was pulled out of the bag. There are 11 possible combinations of silver dollars and quarters in the bag:

- 0 silver dollars, 10 quarters
- 1 silver dollars, 9 quarters
- 2 silver dollars, 8 quarters
- 3 silver dollars, 7 quarters
- 4 silver dollars, 6 quarters
- 5 silver dollars, 5 quarters
- 6 silver dollars, 4 quarters
- 7 silver dollars, 3 quarters

- 8 silver dollars, 2 quarters
- 9 silver dollars, 1 quarters
- 10 silver dollars, 0 quarters

So $P(H) = \frac{1}{11}$, and $P(\overline{H}) = \frac{10}{11}$

$$
\begin{aligned}
P(E|H) &= \frac{1}{10} \\
P(E|\overline{H}) &= \frac{1}{11}\left(\frac{2}{10} + \frac{3}{10} + \frac{4}{10} + \ldots + \frac{10}{10}\right) \\
&= \frac{1}{110}(2 + 3 + 4 + \ldots + 10) \\
&= \frac{54}{110} = \frac{27}{55}
\end{aligned}
$$

$$
\begin{aligned}
P(H|E) &= \frac{P(E|H)P(H)}{P(E|H)P(H) + P(E|\overline{H})P(\overline{H})} \\
&= \frac{\frac{1}{10}\cdot\frac{1}{11}}{\frac{1}{10}\cdot\frac{1}{11} + \frac{54}{110}\cdot\frac{10}{11}} \\
&= \frac{11}{551} = 0.0199637
\end{aligned}
$$

So the odds are about 100 to 2, or 50 to 1, against the silver dollar being the only one in the bag.

Problem 159. One card is removed from a standard pack of 52 playing cards. From the remaining cards two are randomly drawn. If they are both spades then what is the probability the removed card is a spade?

Answer. This is a Bayesian problem. The hypothesis is the removed card is a spade and the evidence is the two drawn cards are spades. The prior probability of the hypothesis is the probability of randomly removing a spade from a full deck. There are 13 spades out of a total of 52 cards so the probability is $P(H) = 13/52 = 1/4$ and the probability the removed card was not a spade is $P(\overline{H}) = 3/4$. Given that the removed card was a spade, the probability of drawing two spades from the remaining 51 cards is $P(E|H) = (12 \cdot 11)/(51 \cdot 50) = 22/425$. and given the removed card was not a spade, the probability is $P(E|\overline{H}) = (13 \cdot 12)/(51 \cdot 50) = 26/425$. Bayes' theorem then says that the probability the removed card is a spade, given the evidence, is

$$
\begin{aligned}
P(H|E) &= \frac{P(E|H)P(H)}{P(E|H)P(H) + P(E|\overline{H})P(\overline{H})} \\
&= \frac{(22/425)(1/4)}{(22/425)(1/4) + (26/425)(3/4)} \\
&= \frac{11}{50}
\end{aligned}
$$

The probability the removed card is a spade goes from $1/4 = 0.25$ before the two cards are drawn to $11/50 = 0.22$ after.

Problem 160. A bag contains 3 red balls and 10 white balls for a total of 13 balls. Spike randomly removes one of the balls but does not show it to anyone. Next Spud removes a ball and notes that it is red. What is the probability that Spike's ball is also red?

Answer. This problem can be solved using Bayes' theorem. The hypothesis, H, is that Spike's ball is red and the evidence, E, is that Spud's ball is red. The prior probability of the hypothesis is the probability that Spike's ball is red before Spud removes a red ball. Initially we know that 3 out of the 13 balls are red so the prior probability is $P(H) = 3/13$. Likewise the prior probability that the hypothesis is false is $P(\overline{H}) = 10/13$. The likelihood of the evidence, given that the hypothesis is true, is $P(E|H) = 2/12 = 1/6$ since if Spike's ball is red then only 2 of the remaining 12 balls are red. Similarly, the likelihood of the evidence given that the hypothesis is false is $P(E|\overline{H}) = 3/12 = 1/4$. Now we can calculate the posterior probability of the hypothesis, given the evidence, using Bayes' theorem:

$$
\begin{aligned}
P(H|E) &= \frac{P(E|H)P(H)}{P(E|H)P(H) + P(E|\overline{H})P(\overline{H})} \\
&= \frac{(1/6)(3/13)}{(1/6)(3/13) + (1/4)(10/13)} \\
&= \frac{1}{6}
\end{aligned}
$$

The evidence has reduced the probability that Spikes ball is red from 3/13 to 1/6.

Problem 161. Continuing with the previous question, suppose that Spud puts his ball back into the bag and now Sparky reaches into the bag and removes a red ball. Now what is the probability that Spike's ball is red?

Answer. We have the additional piece of evidence that Sparky has also removed a red ball. The hypothesis is still that Spike's ball is red with prior probabilities $P(H) = 3/13$ and $P(\overline{H}) = 10/13$. If the hypothesis is true then both Spud and Sparky have a probability of $2/12 = 1/6$ of removing a red ball. The likelihood of the evidence, given that the hypothesis is true, is therefore $P(E|H) = (1/6)^2$. If the hypothesis is false then both Spud and Sparky have a probability of $3/12 = 1/4$ of removing a red ball. The likelihood of the evidence, given that the hypothesis is false, is therefore $P(E|\overline{H}) = (1/4)^2$. Once again using Bayes's theorem, we can calculate the posterior probability.

$$P(H|E) = \frac{(1/6)^2(3/13)}{(1/6)^2(3/13) + (1/4)^2(10/13)}$$
$$= \frac{2}{17}$$

This new evidence has further reduce the probability that Spikes ball is red from $1/6$ to $2/17$.

Problem 162. In the previous question suppose that

Spud did not put his ball back into the bag and that Sparky reached into the bag and also pulled out a red ball. How does this change the probability that Spike's ball is red?

Answer. If Spike's ball is red then Spud's probability for removing a red ball is 1/6 and Sparky's probability for removing a red ball is 1/11 so we have $P(E|H) = (1/6)(1/11) = 1/66$. If Spike's ball is not red then Spud's probability for removing a red ball is 1/4 and Sparky's probability for removing a red ball is 2/11 so we have $P(E|\overline{H}) = (1/4)(2/11) = 1/22$. From Bayes's theorem we get

$$P(H|E) = \frac{(1/66)(3/13)}{(1/66)(3/13) + (1/22)(10/13)}$$
$$= \frac{1}{11}$$

This is the smallest probability so far that Spike's ball is red.

Problem 163. A sign at the supermarket advertises a sale on Mississippi catfish. Two of the letters from the word Mississippi fall off and little Spanky Jr. randomly puts them back up. What is the probability that they were put back in the correct position?

Answer. If they are the same two letters then they are certain to be put back in the correct position. If they are different then there are only two ways they can be put back, one of which is correct, so the probability is $1/2$ that they are put back correctly. The only thing left to do is to calculate the probability that the letters are the same and that they are different. The word Mississippi has four i's, four s's, two p's, and one m. There are $4 \cdot 3 = 12$ ways to get two i's, $4 \cdot 3 = 12$ ways to get two s's, $2 \cdot 1 = 2$ ways to get two p's, and a total of $11 \cdot 10 = 110$ ways to get two letters so the probability of the two letters being the same is $(12 + 12 + 2)/110 = 13/55$. The two letters must either be the same or different, therefore the probability they are different is $1 - 13/55 = 42/55$. The probability of the letters being put back in the correct position is then $(1)(13/55) + (1/2)(42/55) = 34/55$.

Problem 164. Spike has four dice. Two of them are fair, and two of them are loaded, so that the probability of rolling a six is $1/4$, the probability of rolling a one is $1/12$, and the probability of rolling any of the other numbers is $1/6$. Spike can't remember which of the dice are fair so he randomly picks up two and rolls them. If they both turn up six then what is the probability that they are both loaded, both fair, or one fair and one loaded?

Answer. This is a Bayesian problem with three competing hypotheses,
A=both dice are loaded,
B=both dice are fair, and
C=one is fair and one is loaded.
The number of ways Spike could pick two of the four dice is $\binom{4}{2} = 6$. There is only one way to pick both of the loaded dice or both of the fair dice and there are 4 ways to pick one fair and one loaded die. The prior probabilities are therefore $P(A) = P(B) = 1/6$ and $P(C) = 4/6 = 2/3$. The evidence in this case is two sixes were rolled. The likelihood of getting two sixes with the loaded dice is $P(E|A) = (1/4)^2 = 1/16$. The likelihood with the fair dice is $P(E|B) = (1/6)^2 = 1/36$ and the likelihood with one fair and one loaded die is $P(E|C) = (1/6)(1/4) = 1/24$. Let

$$
\begin{aligned}
D &= P(E|A)P(A) + P(E|B)P(B) + P(E|C)P(C) \\
&= 37/864
\end{aligned}
$$

then the posterior probabilities are:

$$
\begin{aligned}
P(A|E) &= \frac{P(E|A)P(A)}{D} \\
&= \frac{(1/16)(1/6)}{37/864} \\
&= \frac{9}{37}
\end{aligned}
$$

$$P(B|E) = \frac{P(E|B)P(B)}{D}$$

$$= \frac{(1/36)(1/6)}{37/864}$$

$$= \frac{4}{37}$$

$$P(C|E) = \frac{P(E|C)P(C)}{D}$$

$$= \frac{(1/24)(2/3)}{37/864}$$

$$= \frac{24}{37}$$

The most likely scenario is that one die is fair and the other loaded, second most likely is they are both loaded, and least likely is they are both fair.

Problem 165. In the previous question, suppose Spike gets a six and a five. How does this change the probabilities?

Answer. The prior probabilities are the same as before: $P(A) = P(B) = 1/6$ and $P(C) = 4/6 = 2/3$. The evidence is now that a six and a five were rolled so the likelihoods will be different. The likelihood with the loaded dice is $P(E|A) = (1/4)(1/6) + (1/6)(1/4) = 1/12$. The likelihood with the fair dice is $P(E|B) = 2(1/6)^2 = 1/18$

and the likelihood with one fair and one loaded die is $P(E|C) = (1/6)(1/4) + (1/6)(1/6) = 5/72$. Let

$$
\begin{aligned}
D &= P(E|A)P(A) + P(E|B)P(B) + P(E|C)P(C) \\
&= 5/72
\end{aligned}
$$

then the posterior probabilities are:

$$
\begin{aligned}
P(A|E) &= \frac{P(E|A)P(A)}{D} \\
&= \frac{(1/12)(1/6)}{5/72} \\
&= \frac{1}{5}
\end{aligned}
$$

$$
\begin{aligned}
P(B|E) &= \frac{P(E|B)P(B)}{D} \\
&= \frac{(1/18)(1/6)}{5/72} \\
&= \frac{2}{15}
\end{aligned}
$$

$$
\begin{aligned}
P(C|E) &= \frac{P(E|C)P(C)}{D} \\
&= \frac{(5/72)(2/3)}{5/72} \\
&= \frac{2}{3}
\end{aligned}
$$

It is now even more likely that one die is fair and the other loaded. It is somewhat less likely that both dice are loaded and somewhat more likely that both are fair.

Problem 166. In the previous question suppose Spike gets a six and a one. How does this change the probabilities?

Answer. The prior probabilities are unchanged. The evidence is now that a six and a one were rolled so the likelihoods are: $P(E|A) = (1/4)(1/12) + (1/12)(1/4) = 1/24$, $P(E|B) = 2(1/6)^2 = 1/18$, $P(E|C) = (1/6)(1/12) + (1/6)(1/4) = 1/18$, and

$$
\begin{aligned}
D &= P(E|A)P(A) + P(E|B)P(B) \\
&\quad + P(E|C)P(C) \\
&= 23/432
\end{aligned}
$$

The posterior probabilities are then:

$$
\begin{aligned}
P(A|E) &= \frac{P(E|A)P(A)}{D} \\
&= \frac{(1/24)(1/6)}{23/432} \\
&= \frac{3}{23}
\end{aligned}
$$

$$P(B|E) \;=\; \frac{P(E|B)P(B)}{D}$$

$$=\; \frac{(1/18)(1/6)}{23/432}$$

$$=\; \frac{4}{23}$$

$$P(C|E) \;=\; \frac{P(E|C)P(C)}{D}$$

$$=\; \frac{(1/18)(2/3)}{23/432}$$

$$=\; \frac{16}{23}$$

This is the highest probability yet that one die is fair and the other loaded. It is almost a toss up between both dice being fair or loaded.

Problem 167. The ten members of the Peewee Valley Model Train Club meet to elect a new president. Each member is as likely to vote for himself as for one of the other members. If Spike gets 5 votes what is the probability that he voted for himself?

Answer. The probability that a member votes for himself is $1/2$, the probability that he votes for someone else is also $1/2$, and the probability that he votes for a particular one of the other 9 members is $(1/2)(1/9) = 1/18$. If Spike voted for himself then he got 4 votes from the other 9 members and the probability of that happening is $\binom{9}{4}(1/18)^4(17/18)^5$. If Spike did not vote for himself then he got 5 votes from the other 9 members with a probability $\binom{9}{5}(1/18)^5(17/18)^4$. Taking the ratio of the probability that 'he did' to 'he did not' vote for himself gives 17. Spike is 17 times more likely than not to have voted for himself.

Problem 168. Bluebeard is known to have hidden a large part of his treasure on one of two Pacific islands named *Palau* and *Nauru*. It is believed to be twice as likely that the island is *Palau* instead of *Nauru*. A set of instructions to the location of the treasure has been found but most of the name of the island is blotted out. Only a letter u can still be recognized. Does this change the probability that the island is *Palau*?

Answer. This is a Bayesian problem. The hypothesis is that the treasure is on *Palau* and the evidence is that one random letter from the name of the island is u. The prior probability is given as $P(H) = 2/3$ and $P(\overline{H}) = 1/3$. The likelihood that a random letter is u given that the island is *Palau* is $P(E|H) = 1/5$. The likelihood that a random letter is u given that the island is *Nauru* is $P(E|\overline{H}) = 2/5$. The posterior probability of the hypothesis, given the evidence is

$$P(H|E) = \frac{(1/5)(2/3)}{(1/5)(2/3) + (2/5)(1/3)}$$
$$= \frac{1}{2}$$

The probability is now a toss up between the islands. Both of them are equally likely.

Problem 169. One of Sparky's nine goats broke loose and ate all of Thelma Lou's sunflowers. Both Spike and Spud saw which goat it was and they both claim it was the white one. Assuming that Spike and Spud respectively tell the truth 75 and 80 percent of the time, what is the probability that it was the white goat.

Answer. This is a Bayesian problem. The hypothesis is the culprit was the white goat. The evidence is that both Spike and Spud say it was the white goat. Assuming that any of the nine goats could have broken loose and eaten the sunflowers, the prior probability that it was the white goat is $P(H) = 1/9$ and the probability it was not is $P(\overline{H}) = 8/9$. Given that it was the white goat, the probability that both Spike and Spud say it was, is the probability they simultaneously tell the truth, $P(E|H) = (3/4)(4/5) = 3/5$. Given that it was not the white goat, the probability they both say it was, is the probability they simultaneously lie and simultaneously lie about it being the white goat. The probability they simultaneously lie is $(1/4)(1/5) = 1/20$ and the probability they both lie about it being the white goat is $(1/8)(1/8) = 1/64$, therefore $P(E|\overline{H}) = (1/20)(1/64) = 1/1280$. The probability that it was the white goat, given that both Spike and Spud say it was, is then

$$
\begin{aligned}
P(H|E) &= \frac{P(E|H)P(H)}{P(E|H)P(H) + P(E|\overline{H})P(\overline{H})} \\
&= \frac{(3/5)(1/9)}{(3/5)(1/9) + (1/1280)(8/9)} \\
&= \frac{96}{97}
\end{aligned}
$$

So the odds are very good that it was the white goat.

Problem 170. Wally, Winky, and Wilbur respectively tell the truth with probabilities 4/5, 3/5, and 5/7. Wally reports that a coin toss came up heads while Winky and Wilbur say it was tails. What is the probability that it was heads?

Answer. This is a Bayesian problem. The hypothesis is that the toss was heads and the evidence is Wally says it was heads but Winky and Wilbur say it was tails. The prior probabilities are $P(H) =$

$1/2$ and $P(\overline{H}) = 1/2$. The probability of the evidence given that it was heads is the probability that Wally told the truth while Winky and Wilbur lied, $P(E|H) = (4/5)(2/5)(2/7) = 16/175$. The probability of the evidence given that it was tails is the probability that Wally lied while Winky and Wilbur told the truth, $P(E|\overline{H}) = (1/5)(3/5)(5/7) = 15/175$. The probability it was heads given the evidence is then

$$
\begin{aligned}
P(H|E) &= \frac{P(E|H)P(H)}{P(E|H)P(H) + P(E|\overline{H})P(\overline{H})} \\
&= \frac{(16/175)(1/2)}{(16/175)(1/2) + (15/175)(1/2)} \\
&= \frac{16}{31}
\end{aligned}
$$

The probability is only slightly better than half that the toss was heads.

Problem 171. Four cards are randomly dealt from a regular pack of 52 cards. Find the probability that there is one card from each suit.

Answer. You can chose one diamond in 13 ways, one heart in 13 ways, one club in 13 ways and one spade in 13 ways so the number of ways to get one of each suit is 13^4. The total number of ways to deal 4 cards (without regard to order) is $\binom{52}{4}$ so the probability is $13^4/\binom{52}{4} = 2197/20825 =$

0.105498. Getting one of each suit should happen a little over 10 percent of the time.

Problem 172. In the previous question what is the probability that no two cards are of equal value. Also what is the probability that there are none of equal value and one of each suit?

Answer. Four cards of different value can be chosen in $\binom{13}{4} = 715$ ways and the suits can be chosen in $4^4 = 256$. The probability of getting four cards of different values is then $715 \cdot 256/\binom{52}{4} = 2816/4165 = .676110$. If only one of each suit is allowed then the suit can be chosen in only $4! = 24$ ways and the probability then drops to $715 \cdot 24/\binom{52}{4} = 264/4165 = 0.063385$.

Problem 173. What is the probability that a 5 card hand, dealt from a regular 52 card deck, contains at least two aces?

Answer. The probability will be 1 minus the probability that the hand has zero or one ace. To get no aces the cards must be chosen from the 48 cards that are not aces. The number of ways to do this is $\binom{48}{5}$. For one ace there are 4 ways to chose it and then $\binom{48}{4}$ ways to chose the remaining 4 cards. The total number of ways to deal a hand of 5 cards is $\binom{52}{5}$. The probability of getting at least two aces is then

$$1 - \frac{\binom{48}{5} + 4\binom{48}{4}}{\binom{52}{5}} = \frac{2257}{54145}$$

Problem 174. In a 5 card hand, dealt from a regular 52 card deck, what is the probability of getting at least one pair?

Answer. The probability will be 1 minus the probability that the hand has no pair. The number of ways to get 5 cards of different values is $\binom{13}{5}$ and the number of ways the suits of the 5 cards can be selected is 4^5. The total number of ways to deal a hand of 5 cards is $\binom{52}{5}$ so the probability is

$$1 - \frac{4^5\binom{13}{5}}{\binom{52}{5}} = \frac{2053}{4165} = 0.492917$$

There is an almost 50 percent chance of getting at least one pair.

Problem 175. In a 5 card hand, dealt from a regular 52 card deck, what is the probability of getting one pair and three singles?

Answer. To get one pair the hand must have 4 unique card values and they can be chosen in $\binom{13}{4}$ ways. For each of these ways the value of the pair can be chosen in 4 ways. The suits for the pair can be chosen in $\binom{4}{2}$ ways and the suits for the three singles can be chosen in 4^3 ways. The total number of ways to get a 5 card hand with one pair and three singles is then $4\binom{13}{4}4^3\binom{4}{2}$. Divide this by the total number of possible hands, $\binom{52}{5}$, to get the probability: $352/833 = 0.422569$. The chance of getting exactly one pair and three singles is just over 42 percent.

Problem 176. In a 5 card hand, dealt from a regular 52 card deck, what is the probability of getting two pair?

Answer. To get two pair the hand must have 3 unique card values and they can be chosen in $\binom{13}{3}$ ways. For each of these ways the value of the single card can be chosen in 3 ways. The suits for each pair can be chosen in $\binom{4}{2}$ ways and the suit for the single can be chosen in 4 ways. The total number of ways to get a 5 card hand with two pairs is then $3\binom{13}{3}4\binom{4}{2}^2$. Divide this by the total number of possible hands, $\binom{52}{5}$, to get the probability: $198/4165 = 0.0475390$. The chance of getting two pair is a little under 5 percent.

Problem 177. In a 5 card hand, dealt from a regular 52 card deck, what is the probability of getting three of a kind and two singles?

Answer. To get three of a kind and two singles the hand must have 3 unique card values and they can be chosen in $\binom{13}{3}$ ways. For each of these ways the value of the three of a kind can be chosen in 3 ways. The suits for the three of a kind can be chosen in 4 ways and the suits for the two singles can be chosen in 4^2 ways. The total number of ways to get a 5 card hand with a three of a kind and two singles is then $3\binom{13}{3}4^3$. Divide this by the total number of possible hands, $\binom{52}{5}$, to get the probability: $88/4165 = 0.0211284$. The chance of getting three of a kind and two singles is just over 2 percent.

Problem 178. In a 5 card hand, dealt from a regular 52 card deck, what is the probability of getting four of a kind?

Answer. To get four of a kind the hand must have 2 unique card values which can be chosen in $\binom{13}{2}$ ways. For each of these ways the value of the four of a kind can be chosen in 2 ways. The suits for the four of a kind can be chosen in 1 way and the suit for the single can be chosen in 4 ways. The total number of ways to get to get a 5 card hand with four of a kind is then $2\binom{13}{2}4$. Divide this by the total number of possible hands, $\binom{52}{5}$, to get the probability: $1/4165 = 0.000240096$.

Problem 179. In the most common form of a card

game called Poker each player is dealt 5 cards from a regular 52 card deck. The highest ranking hands in the game are called straights. A straight consists of five cards with consecutive values. If the cards are also of the same suit then the hand is called a straight flush. The lowest set of consecutive values are: Ace, 2, 3, 4, 5. The highest set of values are: 10, jack, queen, king, ace. Calculate the probabilities of getting a straight flush and just a straight.

Answer. The one peculiarity with this calculation is that the ace can act as both the lowest card and the highest card so there are effectively 14 card values and 10 ways of having 5 consecutive values. For a straight flush the cards all have to be of the same suit so there are 4 possibilities for the suit. The number of ways to get a straight flush is then $10 \cdot 4 = 40$ and the number of 5 card hands is $\binom{52}{5}$ so the probability is $40/\binom{52}{5} = 0.00001539$. For a regular straight each card can be any of the four suits so in general there are 4^5 possibilities for the suits but in 4 of these all the cards are of the same suit which would make it a straight flush. The number of regular straights is then $10(4^5 - 4)$ and the probability of getting a regular straight is $10(4^5 - 4)/\binom{52}{5} = 0.003925$.

Problem 180. Spike and Spud are playing regular 5 card poker with a 52 card deck. Spike has four of a kind and he wants to know the probability that Spud also has four of a kind. Help him out with the calculation.

Answer. There are 11 possible values for Spud's four of a kind and then there are $52 - 5 - 4 = 43$ remaining cards that can be used to complete the hand. The number of ways Spud can have a four of a kind is $11 \cdot 43 = 473$ and the total number of possible hands he can have is $\binom{47}{5}$. The probability that Spud has four of a kind is then $473/\binom{47}{5} = 1/3243 = 0.00030836$.

Problem 181. In the previous question, instead of four of a kind, Spike has three of a kind and he wants to know the probability that Spud has a full house (three of a kind and a pair) or four of a kind. Help him out with the calculation.

Answer. First look at the probability that Spud has a four of a kind. There are 10 possible values for the four of a kind with $52 - 5 - 4 = 43$ cards left to complete the hand. The number of ways that Spud could have a four of a kind is $10 \cdot 43 = 430$. Calculating the number of ways Spud can have a full house is more difficult. In terms of card values let Spike's hand be represented by *aaabc* and Spud's hand by *dddee*. There are four cases that have to be counted separately. First if d, e, b, and c are all different values then there are

$10 \cdot 9 = 90$ ways to chose the values of d and e and $4\binom{4}{2} = 24$ ways to choose the suits for a total of $90 \cdot 24 = 2160$ ways to construct the hand. If d and e have the same values as b and c then there are 2 ways to choose the d value and for each of these ways there are 3 ways to choose the e suits for a total of $2 \cdot 3 = 6$ ways to complete the hand. If d is equal to b or c and e is different from b or c then there are 2 ways to choose the value of d, 10 ways to choose the value of e and $\binom{4}{2} = 6$ ways to choose the suits for a total of $2 \cdot 10 \cdot 6 = 120$ ways to complete the hand. If e is equal to b or c and d is different from b or c then there are 2 ways to choose the value of e and 3 ways to choose the suits, there are 10 ways to choose the value of d, and 4 ways to choose the suits for a total of $2 \cdot 3 \cdot 10 \cdot 4 = 240$ ways to complete the hand. The total number of ways that Spud can have a full house is then $2160 + 6 + 120 + 240 = 2526$, and the number of ways he can have a full house or a four of a kind is $2526 + 430 = 2956$. The probability that Spud has a full house or a four of a kind is $2956/\binom{47}{5} = 2956/1533939 = 0.00192706$.

Problem 182. The Ballot Problem. Spike and Spud are running for a seat on the Peewee Valley water board. Spike ends up winning the election with a votes to Spud's b votes. During the counting of the votes, Spike is always ahead of Spud. Assuming that the ballots are counted in random order, show that the probability of this happening is $\frac{a-b}{a+b}$.

Answer. The total number of ways the $a + b$ ballots can be counted is $\binom{a+b}{a}$. To find how many ways there are with Spike always ahead of Spud it helps to look at the counting process as a random walk. The walk starts at the origin (point 0). Every vote for Spike is a step to the right, and every vote for Spud is a step to the left. As the votes are counted the walk moves randomly left and right and eventually ends $a - b$ steps to the right of the origin. The total number of walks equals the total number of ways the ballots can be counted, $\binom{a+b}{a}$. The counts where Spike is always ahead of Spud are walks that start with a step to the right and never return to the origin. To find how many of these walks there are, we first have to find the number of walks that start with a step to the right and the number that start with a step to the left. For a walk that begins with a right step, there are $a + b - 1$ steps remaining of which $a - 1$ are to the right, so the number of such walks is $\binom{a+b-1}{a-1} = \binom{a+b-1}{b}$. Likewise the number of walks that begin with a step to the left is $\binom{a+b-1}{b-1} = \binom{a+b-1}{a}$. Now note that every walk that starts with a step to the left must eventually return to the origin. If you reverse the steps of such a walk up to the point where it returns to the origin, then it becomes a walk that starts with a step to the right and returns to the origin. There is a one to one correspondence between origin returning walks that start with a step to the right and those that start with a step to the left. So the number of walks that start with a step to the right and don't return to the origin is equal to the difference

$$\binom{a+b-1}{b} - \binom{a+b-1}{a} = \frac{a-b}{a+b}\binom{a+b}{a}$$

If you divide this difference by the total number of walks, you get the probability that Spike is always ahead of Spud. The probability is $\frac{a-b}{a+b}$. Let's say it was a close election with Spike getting 510 votes and Spud getting 490 then the probability is $20/1000 = 1/50 = 0.02$ which makes what happened unlikely. Maybe the Sheriff should investigate?

Problem 183. Newton-Pepys Problem. Samuel Pepys once asked Isaac Newton which of the following events had the highest probability:

- A = throwing 6 dice and getting at least one six

- B = throwing 12 dice and getting at least two sixes

- C = throwing 18 dice and getting at least three sixes

Pepys thought C had the highest probability but Newton set him straight and told him A had the highest probability. What are the probabilities of A, B, and C?

Answer. Each of the dice have 6 faces so if you throw N dice there are 6^N possible outcomes. The number of outcomes with no six on any of the dice is 5^N. The number of outcomes with one of the dice showing a six is $N \cdot 5^{N-1}$. In general it's not hard to see that the number of outcomes with k of the dice showing a six is $\binom{N}{k}5^{N-k}$. Using this result the probabilities for A, B, and C can be written as ratios of favorable to total number of outcomes.

$$P(A) = \frac{6^6 - 5^6}{6^6} = \frac{31031}{46656} = 0.665102$$

$$P(B) = \frac{6^{12} - 5^{12} - 12 \cdot 5^{11}}{6^{12}} = \frac{1346704211}{2176782336}$$
$$= 0.618667$$

$$P(C) = \frac{6^{18} - 5^{18} - 18 \cdot 5^{17} - 153 \cdot 5^{16}}{6^{18}}$$
$$= \frac{15166600495229}{25389989167104} = 0.597346$$

Problem 184. To win the Tiddlywinks tournament Spike has to win two consecutive games out of three. He must play alternate games against two opponents, Spud and Wilbur. Spud is a former champion and is considered to be a much better player than Wilbur. Show that Spike's best strategy is to start by playing his first game against Spud.

Answer. Let x and y be the probabilities that Spike wins against Spud and Wilbur respectively. Since Spud is a more skillful Tiddlywinker than Wilbur, we must assume $x < y$. If he starts by playing Spud then his chances of winning the tournament are $xy + (1 - x)xy = xy(2 - x)$. If he starts by playing Wilbur then his chances are $yx + (1 - y)xy = xy(2 - y)$. The ratio of these probabilities is $(2 - x)/(2 - y)$ which is greater than 1 as long as $x < y$. So Spike has a higher probability of becoming champion if he starts by playing Spud.

Problem 185. When Spike and Spud play chess, Spud has a 75 percent chance of winning if he has the first move and only a 60 percent chance otherwise. At the beginning of each game they flip a coin to see who goes first. If the only thing you know is that Spud has just won a game, then what is the probability that he had the first move?

Answer. This is a Bayesian problem. The hypothesis is that Spud had the first move and the evidence is that he won the game. The prior probability of the hypothesis is $P(H) = P(\overline{H}) = 1/2$. The likelihood of the evidence given the hypothesis is $P(E|H) = 3/4$ and the likelihood given the hypothesis is not true is $P(E|\overline{H}) = 3/5$. The posterior probability of the hypothesis is then

$$P(H|E) = \frac{(1/2)(3/4)}{(1/2)(3/4) + (1/2)(3/5)}$$
$$= \frac{5}{9}$$

Problem 186. Craps: Craps is a gambling game played with two dice. One of the most popular bets in Craps is called the pass bet. It starts with the player making a first roll of the dice, getting a sum S for the two faces. The player wins on the first roll if S is 7 or 11 and loses if S is 2, 3, or 12. If S is 4, 5, 6, 8, 9, or 10 then this becomes what is known as the point and the player continues rolling the dice until either the point reappears and he wins or a 7 appears and he loses. What is the probability of winning this bet?

Answer. Let P_S be the probability that the sum of the two dice is S. These probabilities were calculated in a previous question to be $P_2 = P_{12} = 1/36$, $P_3 = P_{11} = 2/36 = 1/18$, $P_4 = P_{10} = 3/36 = 1/12$, $P_5 = P_9 = 4/36 = 1/9$, $P_6 = P_8 = 5/36$, $P_7 = 6/36 = 1/6$. The probability that the player wins on the first roll is $P_7 + P_{11} = 2/9$. If a point X is established on the first roll then the player wins on the second roll if X comes up again. This has probability P_X^2. If neither X nor 7 appear on the second roll and X appears on the third roll then he wins. The probability of this happening is $P_X(1 - P_7 - P_X)P_X$. In general the probability of winning on roll $k \geq 2$ is $P_X(1 - P_7 - P_X)^{k-2}P_X$. Summing these terms over all values of k gives the probability of winning after the first roll given that the point is X.

$$Q_X = P_X^2 \sum_{k=0}^{\infty}(1 - P_7 - P_X)^k = \frac{P_X^2}{P_7 + P_X}$$

The values of Q_X are $Q_4 = Q_{10} = 1/36$, $Q_5 = Q_9 = 2/45$, and $Q_6 = Q_8 = 25/396$. The overall probability of winning the pass bet is then:

$$\frac{2}{9} + 2(Q_4 + Q_5 + Q_6) = 244/495 = 0.492929$$

which is just slightly below 50 percent.

Problem 187. Spike buys a lottery ticket that has 5 unique numbers between 1 and 32. In the lottery drawing, 5 unique numbers between 1 and 32 will be randomly selected. What is the probability that there are 0, 1, 2, 3, 4, or 5 matches between the numbers on Spike's ticket and the lottery drawing numbers?

Answer. In general there are $\binom{N}{n}$ ways to select n numbers from N when the selection order does not matter. This is the number of possible lottery tickets and the number of possible lottery drawings. To get m matches in a drawing, the m matching numbers have to be drawn from the n ticket numbers and the remaining nm numbers have to be drawn from the numbers not on the ticket. The number of ways to do this is $M(m) = \binom{N-n}{n-m}\binom{n}{m}$. Dividing this by the total number of tickets gives the probability of getting m matches.

$$P(m) = \frac{\binom{N-n}{n-m}\binom{n}{m}}{\binom{N}{n}}$$

In Spike's case the numbers are $N = 32$ and $n = 5$ so the probabilities are:

$$P(0) = \frac{40365}{100688} = 0.400892$$

$$P(1) = \frac{43875}{100688} = 0.435752$$

$$P(2) = \frac{14625}{100688} = 0.145251$$

$$P(3) = \frac{1755}{100688} = 0.0174301$$

$$P(4) = \frac{135}{201376} = 0.000670388$$

$$P(5) = \frac{1}{201376} = 0.00000496583$$

Spike is more likely to match one number than he is to match no numbers. He has an almost 60 percent chance of matching at least one number.

Problem 188. A coffee shop gives everyone who buys a coffee a scratch-off ticket. There are 5 different kinds of tickets and if you collect all 5 you get a prize. Assuming you have an equal chance of getting any one of the 5 kinds of tickets when you buy a coffee, how many coffees do you have to buy on average to collect all the tickets?

Answer. This is a collection problem. You collect the first ticket right away when you buy your first coffee. On the second coffee there is a $1/5$ probability you will get the same ticket you already have and a $4/5$ probability you will get a new one. Once you have a second unique ticket then the probability of getting a new ticket on the next purchase will be $3/5$ and so on. In general once you have collected k unique tickets, the probability of getting a new one on the next purchase is $p_k = (5 - k)/5$. Let X_k be the number of coffees needed to get a new ticket once k unique tickets have been collected. X_k is a geometric random variable because the probability that $X_k = m$ is given by $p_k q_k^{m-1}$. The average value of a geometric random variable with success probability p_k is

$1/p_k$ (see the Spike goes fishing problem). This means that it takes, on average, $1/p_k = 5/(5-k)$ coffees to get a new ticket once you already have k unique tickets. The number of tickets needed to collect all 5 kinds is $N = X_0 + X_1 + X_2 + X_3 + X_4$ so to get the average we just sum the averages for each X_k. This gives:

$$E[N] = \frac{5}{5} + \frac{5}{4} + \frac{5}{3} + \frac{5}{2} + \frac{5}{1} = \frac{137}{12} = 11.42$$

which can be written more succinctly as $E[N] = 5H_5$ where H_5 is called the fifth harmonic number. In general the nth harmonic number is defined as:

$$H_n = \sum_{k=1}^{n} \frac{1}{k}$$

The problem can then be extended to the general case where we want to collect n tickets. The average number of coffees that you need to buy in this case is $E[N] = nH_n$.

Problem 189. Birthday Problem 1: In a group of n people what is the probability that at least two of them have the same birthday? How many people does it take for the probability to be greater than 50 percent?

Answer. To solve this problem we make two simplifying assumptions. First assume that all years have

365 days i.e. ignore leap years and the possibility of a February 29 birthday. Second assume that all birthdays are equally likely. This is not exactly true but it's a close enough approximation. It is easier to solve the problem by first calculating the probability that everyone has a different birthday and then subtracting this from 1 to get the probability of at least two people having the same birthday. For everyone to have different birthdays there are 365 choices for the first person, 364 for the second, 363 for the third, and so on. The total ways n people can have different birthdays is then $365(365-1)(365-2)\cdots(365-n+1)$. The total ways n people can have birthdays without restriction is 365^n so the probability that everyone has different birthdays is $q(n) = 365(365-1)(365-2)\cdots(365-n+1)/365^n$ and the probability that at least two people have the same birthday is $p(n) = 1 - q(n)$. Trying different values of n gives $p(22) = 0.475695$ and $p(23) = 0.538344$ so it takes at least 23 people to get a greater than 50 percent chance of having two or more people with the same birthday.

Problem 190. Birthday Problem 2: In the above birthday problem, we were looking for any match in birthdays among n people. Now we want to find the probability of one particular match in a group of n people. Let's say for example, you are in a room with n other people. What is the probability that at least one other person in the room has the same birthday as you? How many people need to be in the room for the probability to exceed 50 percent?

Answer. The probability that any person in the room does not have your birthday is $364/365$ and the probability that all n of them do not is $(364/365)^n$. The probability that at least one other person in the room has your birthday is then $p(n) = 1 - (364/365)^n$. The probabilities for various values of n are: $p(100) = 0.239933$, $p(200) = 0.422298$, $p(300) = 0.560908$, $p(400) = 0.666260$, $p(500) = 0.746335$. It takes at least 400 people to have a roughly $2/3$ probability of someone else having your birthday. At $n = 253$ we have $p(253) = 0.500477$ so it takes at least 253 people to have a 50 percent chance of finding someone with your birthday.

Problem 191. Birthday Problem 3: On average, how many people do you need so that for every day of the year there is at least one person with that birthday?

Answer. Obviously the number of people will have to be much larger than 365 but how much larger? The key to solving this is to look at it as a collection problem. The object is to keep adding randomly selected people to our collection until we have collected all 365 birthdays. Let the random variable X_k be the number of new people that have to be added to get a new birthday given that k unique birthdays have been collected so far. X_k is a geometric random variable with probability $P(X_k = m) = p_k q_k^{m-1}$ where $p_k = (365 - k)/365$ is the probability of getting a new birthday once k have already been collected and $q_k = 1 - p_k$. If N is the number of people needed to get all 365 birthdays then:

$$N = X_0 + X_1 + X_2 + \cdots + X_{364}$$

The average (expectation) of N is just the sum of the averages of the X_k and those averages are $E[X_k] = 1/p_k = 365/(365 - k)$ therefore

$$E[N] = 365 \sum_{k=1}^{365} \frac{1}{k}$$

The sum in this equation is the Harmonic number (see collection problem) H_{365}. The sum is not hard to evaluate on a computer but you can also use the approximation

$$H_n \approx \ln n + \gamma + \frac{1}{2n}$$

where $\gamma = 0.5772156649$ is called the Euler-Mascheroni constant. The approximation is very good for

$n = 365$. The calculation of $E[N]$ with the approximation is 2364.64625 while the exact calculation is 2364.64602. In any case, the conclusion is that you will need about 2365 people to have at least one of each birthday.

Problem 192. Birthday Problem 4: What is the probability that in a group of $r \geq 365$ people there will be at least one birthday for every day of the year? What is the minimum value of r so that the probability is greater than 50 percent?

Answer. The key to solving this problem is to look at it in terms of randomly putting r balls into $n = 365$ boxes. In our case we are putting randomly chosen people into boxes that correspond to their birthdays. In nonexclusive probabilities, a formula is derived for the probability that when r balls are randomly placed into n boxes, each box will have at least one ball. We can use that formula here. With $n = 365$, we have for the probability that a group of r people have at least one birthday for every day of the year:

$$P(r) = \sum_{i=0}^{365}(-1)^i \binom{365}{i}(1 - i/365)^r$$

Trying some values for r in this equation gives $P(2286) = 0.499414$ and $P(2287) = 0.500371$ so we need at least 2287 people to have a better than 50 percent chance of having one birthday for every day of the year.

Problem 193. To save money Spike gets a monkey to do the payroll for his business. The computer prints out paychecks and envelopes and the monkey randomly puts paychecks into envelopes and mails them. If Spike has 10 employees, what is the probability that at least one of them gets the correct paycheck? What is the probability that no one gets their correct paycheck.

Answer. We will solve this for the general case of n employees. The probability can be found using the procedure outlined in nonexclusive probabilities for calculating the probability of nonexclusive events. The individual events in this case are that a particular employee gets the correct check. Let A_i be the event that employee i gets a correct check, then the probability of at least one employee getting a correct check is $P(A_1 \cup A_2 \cup \cdots A_n)$. Equation 41 of nonexclusive probabilities shows how to calculate this probability. The inner sum in this equation requires the probability that a particular group of k employees gets correct checks. If a single employee gets a correct check there are $(n-1)!$ ways the rest of the checks can be distributed and a total of $n!$ ways to distribute all the checks so the probability is $P(A_i) = (n-1)!/n!$. The event $A_i \cap A_j$ occurs when both employee i and j get correct checks. The probability of this happening is $P(A_i \cap A_j) = (n-2)!/n!$. In general the probability that a particular group of k employees gets correct checks is $(n-k)!/n!$. There are $\binom{n}{k}$ groups of k employees so the inner sum of equation 41 is

$$\binom{n}{k} \frac{(n-k)!}{n!} = \frac{1}{k!}$$

The probability that at least one employee gets a correct check is then:

$$P(A_1 \cup A_2 \cup \cdots A_n) = \sum_{k=1}^{n} \frac{(-1)^{k-1}}{k!}$$

For $n = 10$ the probability is $28319/44800 = 0.632121$ so the monkey has a pretty good chance of getting at least one paycheck correct. The probability that no one gets a correct check is just 1 minus this or $16481/44800 = 0.367879$. In general for n employees, let $P_0(n)$ be the probability that none of n employees gets the correct paycheck then the formula for $P_0(n)$ is:

$$P_0(n) = \sum_{k=0}^{n} \frac{(-1)^k}{k!}$$

Problem 194. In the previous problem calculate the probability that exactly 1, 2, 3, and 4 employees get correct paychecks.

Answer. We will first solve for the probability that exactly m out of n employees get correct paychecks. There are $\binom{n}{m}$ ways to choose the m out of n employees that get correct paychecks and for each of these ways there are $(n-m)!P_0(n-m)$ ways that none of the remaining $n-m$ people get correct checks where the formula for $P_0(n)$ comes from the previous question. The total number of ways that exactly m out of n employees can get correct paychecks is then $\binom{n}{m}(n-m)!P_0(n-m)$. Dividing this by $n!$ gives the probability:

$$
\begin{aligned}
P_m(n) &= \binom{n}{m}\frac{(n-m)!}{n!}P_0(n-m) \\
&= \frac{P_0(n-m)}{m!}
\end{aligned}
$$

Using $n = 10$ the probabilities for various values of m are:

$$P_0(10) = \frac{16481}{44800} = 0.367879$$

$$P_1(10) = \frac{16687}{45360} = 0.367879$$

$$P_2(10) = \frac{2119}{11520} = 0.183941$$

$$P_3(10) = \frac{103}{1680} = 0.061309$$

$$P_4(10) = \frac{53}{3456} = 0.015336$$

Problem 195. Three independent events have probability p_1, p_2, and p_3. If e_i is the probability that event i occurs and the other two do not, then show that $p_i = e_i/(e_i + x)$ where x is a solution of the equation $(e_1 + x)(e_2 + x)(e_3 + x) = x^2$.

Answer. By definition $e_1 = p_1(1 - p_2)(1 - p_3)$, $e_2 = (1 - p_1)p_2(1 - p_3)$, and $e_3 = (1 - p_1)(1 - p_2)p_3$. Multiply the first equation by $(1-p_1)/p_1$ the second by $(1 - p_2)/p_2$ and the third by $(1 - p_3)/p_3$ then for all i we have

$$\frac{e_i(1 - p_i)}{p_i} = (1 - p_1)(1 - p_2)(1 - p_3) = x$$

where x is a constant. Solving for p_i gives $p_i = e_i/(e_i + x)$ and substituting this into $(1 - p_1)(1 - p_2)(1 - p_3) = x$ and simplifying shows that x is a solution of $(e_1 + x)(e_2 + x)(e_3 + x) = x^2$.

Problem 196. At a Christmas party Spike, Spud, and Sparky have three gifts to choose from. Two of the gifts are Yosemite Sam mud flaps and one is a bottle of Elvis Presley cologne. Spike really wants the cologne, Sparky wants the mud flaps, and Spud doesn't care what he gets. Spike knows Sparky wants the mud flaps and he also knows that Sparky helped wrap the gifts so he knows which ones have the mud flaps. Spike chooses his gift first, then Sparky chooses his and Spud gets the last one left. Just as they are getting ready to open the gifts, Spike has a brain tornado and asks to swap gifts with Spud. He thinks there is a higher probability that Spud has the gift with the Elvis cologne. Is he right?

Answer. At the last moment Spike realized that if his initial pick was mud flaps then Sparky picked the other set of mud flaps and Spud ended up with the cologne. This was the most likely scenario since Spike had a 2/3 probability of initially picking mud flaps and only a 1/3 probability of initially picking the cologne. It was therefore twice as likely that Spud had the cologne and not him. Asking Spud to switch gifts is the smart thing to do.

Problem 197. Spud's sock drawer has ten pairs of socks. One morning before dawn he goes fumbling through the drawer looking for a pair of socks to go on a hiking trip. He randomly pulls out four socks. What is the probability that he gets at least one matching pair?

Answer. The four socks he selects could consist of zero, one, or two matching pair. The easiest thing to do is to calculate the probability of getting zero pair and then subtract this from 1 to get the probability of at least one pair. For zero matching pair one sock must be selected from four different pairs. The four different pairs can be chosen in $\binom{10}{4}$ ways and there are two socks to choose from in each pair so the number of ways to get zero pair is $\binom{10}{4}2^4 = 3360$. The total number of ways he can select 4 socks is $\binom{20}{4} = 4845$ so the probability of zero matching pairs is $3360/4845 = 224/323$. The probability of at least one matching pair is then $1 - 224/323 = 99/323 = 0.3065$.

Problem 198. Spike and Spud are playing a coin tossing game. They toss a fair coin and if it comes up heads, Spud gives Spike one dollar. If it comes up tails, Spike gives Spud one dollar. Spike starts out with four dollars and Spud starts out with six. The game stops whenever one of them runs out of money in which case we say they are ruined. What are Spike and Spud's chances of being ruined?

Answer. We will solve the problem for the general case where Spike starts with x dollars and Spud starts with y dollars. Let r_k be the probability of ruin when a player (Spike or Spud) has k dollars. This could be the amount he starts with or simply the amount he has at some point during the game. If the player wins the next coin toss, his probability of ruin becomes r_{k+1} and if he loses it becomes r_{k-1}. This means the ruin probabilities must be related as follows: $r_k = (1/2)r_{k+1} + (1/2)r_{k-1}$, where we use $1/2$ for the probability of winning and losing since the coin is fair. r_k is a simple average of r_{k-1} and r_{k+1}. The only way this is possible is if $r_k = ak + b$ for some constants a and b. The value of these constants can be determined given values of r_k for two different values of k. We know that $r_0 = 1$ since by definition if a player has no money he is ruined. If $N = x+y$ is the total amount of money the two players start with, then $r_N = 0$ because if a player has all the money then he cannot be ruined. Using these "boundary values" we find that $b = 1$ and $a = -1/N$. The probability of ruin is then given by the linear function:

$$r_k = 1 - \frac{k}{N}$$

In the specific case where Spike starts with four dollars and Spud starts with six we have $N = 4 + 6 = 10$. Spike's probability of ruin is $r_4 = 1 - 4/10 = 3/5 = 0.6$ and Spud's probability is $r_6 = 1 - 6/10 = 2/5 = 0.4$.

Problem 199. Suppose that in the previous problem the boys are using a funny coin that's not quite fair. If the probability of heads is p and the probability of tails is $q = 1 - p$ how does this change the ruin probabilities?

Answer. Let r_k be Spike's probability of ruin when he has k dollars. He wins a dollar with probability p and loses a dollar with probability $q =$

$1 - p$. If he wins, his ruin probability becomes r_{k+1} and if he loses, it becomes r_{k-1}. The ruin probabilities must therefore obey the equation: $r_k = pr_{k+1} + qr_{k-1}$. This can be solved by assuming r_k to be an exponential function of k. If we make r_k proportional to z^k in the equation, then we find two possible values for z, $z = 1$ and $z = q/p$. The solution for r_k must therefore be of the form $r_k = a(q/p)^k + b$ for some constants a and b. As in the previous problem, we can find the value of these constants using the "boundary values" $r_0 = 1$ and $r_N = 0$ where $N = x + y$ is the sum of the amount of money Spike and Spud start with. Solving for a and b we get the final solution for Spike's ruin probability:

$$r_k = \frac{(q/p)^k - (q/p)^N}{1 - (q/p)^N}$$

Likewise if s_k is Spud's probability of ruin when he has k dollars then, following the same procedure as above, we find that:

$$s_k = \frac{(p/q)^k - (p/q)^N}{1 - (p/q)^N}$$

As in the previous problem, assume that Spike starts with four dollars and Spud starts with six so that $N = 4 + 6 = 10$. If the coin is biased toward heads with $p = 0.6$ then Spike's ruin probability is $r_4 = 0.183369$ and Spud's ruin probability is $s_6 = 0.816631$. With the biased coin Spike's ruin probability has decreased significantly while Spud's has increased as you would expect.

Problem 200. Spud plans to roll a pair of dice until all six possible doubles have shown up. How many rolls will it take him on average?

Answer. This is a collection problem where we are trying to collect all six doubles. It differs a bit from other collection problems since every roll is not necessarily a double. This means that the first double may not come on the first roll. There are 36 possible outcomes when rolling a pair of dice of which six are doubles. The probability of getting the first double is therefore $p_0 = 6/36 = 1/6$ and the average number of rolls required to get the first double is $1/p_0 = 6$. The probability of getting the next double is $p_1 = 5/36$ and the average number of rolls required to get it is $1/p_1 = 36/5$. In general the probability of getting the next double after k doubles have appeared is $p_k = (6 - k)/36$ and the average number of rolls required to get it is $1/p_k = 36/(6-k)$. The average number of rolls required to get all 6 doubles is then

$$\sum_{k=0}^{5} \frac{36}{6 - k} = 36H_6 = \frac{441}{5} = 88.2$$

where H_6 is the sixth harmonic number. Spud

will have to roll the pair of dice on average about 88 times to get all six doubles.

Problem 201. Lewis Carroll Pillow Problem 5: A bag contains one ball that is equally likely to be white or black. A white ball is put in the bag. The bag is shaken and a ball is randomly removed. If the ball is white, what is the probability that the original ball was white.

Answer. This is a Bayesian problem where the hypothesis is that the original ball is white. The prior probability of the hypothesis and its negation are $P(H) = P(\overline{H}) = 1/2$. The evidence is that a white ball was drawn from the bag after a white ball was put in. Given that the original ball was white, the probability of the evidence would be, $P(E|H) = 1$. Given that the original ball was black, the probability of the evidence would be $P(E|\overline{H}) = 1/2$. The posterior probability is then:

$$
\begin{aligned}
P(H|E) &= \frac{P(E|H)P(H)}{P(E|H)P(H) + P(E|\overline{H})P(\overline{H})} \\
&= \frac{(1)(1/2)}{(1)(1/2) + (1/2)(1/2)} \\
&= \frac{2}{3}
\end{aligned}
$$

The probability of the original ball being white has increased from 1/2 to 2/3.

Problem 202. Lewis Carroll Pillow Problem 19: Three bags contain respectively one, two, and three white balls plus each bag has a single black ball. The bags are unmarked and there is no way to determine how many balls a bag has. Two of the bags are randomly chosen and one ball is drawn from each. If one of the balls is white and the other black, what is the probability of drawing a white ball from the remaining bag?

Answer. This is a Bayesian problem where the evidence is that a white ball was drawn from one bag and a black ball from another. We want the probability of drawing a white ball from the remaining bag given this evidence. Let X_i be the event that the remaining bag is the one with i white balls where $i = 1, 2, 3$. The prior probabilities are $P(X_1) = P(X_2) = P(X_3) = 1/3$, i.e. without the evidence the remaining bag is equally likely to have one, two, or three white balls. Let $P(W_i)$ and $P(B_i)$ be the probabilities of drawing a white and black ball respectively from the bag with i white balls then we have $P(W_1) = P(B_1) = 1/2$, $P(W_2) = 2/3$, $P(B_2) = 1/3$, $P(W_3) = 3/4$, $P(B_3) = 1/4$. The likelihood functions are:

$$P(E|X_1) = P(W_2)P(B_3) + P(B_2)P(W_3) = 5/12$$

$$P(E|X_2) = P(W_1)P(B_3) + P(B_1)P(W_3) = 1/2$$

$$P(E|X_3) = P(W_1)P(B_2) + P(B_1)P(W_2) = 1/2$$

Let $D =$

$$P(E|X_1)P(X_1) + P(E|X_2)P(X_2) + P(E|X_3)P(X_3)$$

$= 17/36$, then the posterior probabilities are

$$P(X_1|E) = P(E|X_1)P(X_1)/D = 5/17$$

$$P(X_2|E) = P(E|X_2)P(X_2)/D = 6/17$$

$$P(X_3|E) = P(E|X_3)P(X_3)/D = 6/17$$

The probability of drawing a white ball from the remaining bag given the evidence is then

$$P(W|E) =$$
$$P(W_1)P(X_1|E) + P(W_2)P(X_2|E) +$$
$$P(W_3)P(X_3|E)$$
$$= \frac{11}{17}$$

Further Reading

- *Schaum's Outline of Combinatorics*, V.K. Balakrishnan

- *Problems and Snapshots from the World of Probability*, Blom, Holst and Sandell

- *An Introduction to Probability Theory and its Applications*, William Feller

- *Probability and Random Processes*, Grimmett and Stirzaker

- *One Thousand Exercises in Probability*, Grimmett and Stirzaker

- *The Coin Toss: The Hydrogen Atom of Probability*, Hollos and Hollos

- *Combinatorics Problems and Solutions*, Hollos and Hollos

- *Probability Theory: Principles and Elementary Applications v.1: The Logic of Science*, E. T. Jaynes

- *Fifty Challenging Problems in Probability: With Solutions*, Frederick Mosteller

- *Digital Dice: Computational Solutions to Practical Probability Problems*, Paul J. Nahin

- *Duelling Idiots and Other Probability Puzzlers*, Paul J. Nahin

- *Probabilities: The Little Numbers That Rule Our Lives*, Peter Olofsson

- *Schaum's Outline of Probability and Statistics, 4th edition*, Schiller, Srinivasan and Spiegel

- *Choice and Chance with 1000 Exercises, 5th edition*, William Allen Whitworth

Acknowledgements

In ordinary life we hardly realize that we receive a great deal more than we give, and that it is only with gratitude that life becomes rich. It is very easy to overestimate the importance of our own achievements in comparison with what we owe to others.

Dietrich Bonhoeffer, letter to parents from prison, Sept. 13, 1943

We'd like to thank our parents for helping us in many ways.

We thank the makers and maintainers of all the software we've used in the production of this book: the Emacs text editor, Emacs Calc, the LaTex typsetting system, Inkscape, Evince document viewer, POV-Ray, Maxima computer algebra system, gcc, Guile, awk, z-shell, and the Linux operating system.

Particular thanks to Friedrich A. Lohmueller for his tutorial on making skies in POV-Ray, and to Jerry Stratton for his tutorials on making dice in POV-Ray.

Stefan Hollos and **J. Richard Hollos** are physicists by training, and enjoy anything related to probability. They are the authors of

- **Combinatorics Problems and Solutions**

- **The Coin Toss: The Hydrogen Atom of Probability**

- **Pairs Trading: A Bayesian Example**

- **Simple Trading Strategies That Work**

- **Bet Smart: The Kelly System for Gambling and Investing**

- **The QuantWolf Guide to Calculating Bond Default Probabilities**

- **The Mathematics of Lotteries: How to Calculate the Odds**

- **Signals from the Subatomic World: How to Build a Proton Precession Magnetometer**

They are brothers and business partners at Exstrom Laboratories LLC in Longmont, Colorado. The websites for their work are Exstrom.com and QuantWolf.com.

Thank You

Thank you for buying this book.

If you bought this book from a retailer, register it with us and receive news on updates, special offers, and related products. Just go to

http://www.abrazol.com/books/probability1/

and enter your email address.

4899031R00103

Printed in Great Britain
by Amazon.co.uk, Ltd.,
Marston Gate.